Other titles in the Project

UNIVERSITY OF BATH · SCIENCE 16-19

Project Director: J. J. Thompson, CBE

ELECTRONICS

JACKIE ADAMS
ROBERT HUTCHINGS

Nelson

Thomas Nelson and Sons Ltd
Nelson House   Mayfield Road
Walton-on-Thames   Surrey
KT12 5PL   UK

Thomas Nelson Australia
102 Dodds Street
South Melbourne
Victoria 3205   Australia

Nelson Canada
1120 Birchmount Road
Scarborough   Ontario
M1K 5G4   Canada

I(T)P Thomas Nelson is an International Thomson Publishing Company.

I(T)P is used under licence.

ISBN 017-448251-5

Printed in Great Britain by Hobbs the Printers Ltd, Totton, Hampshire.

Contents

The Project: an introduction

The **University of Bath Science 16–19 Project** grew out of a reappraisal of how far sixth form science had travelled during a period of unprecedented curriculum reform and from an attempt to evaluate future development. Changes were occurring both within the constitution of 16–19 syllabuses themselves and as a result of external pressures from 16+ and from below: syllabus redefinition (starting with the common cores), the introduction of AS-level and its academic recognition, the originally optimistic outcome to the Higginson enquiry, new emphasis on skills and processes and the balance of continuous and final assessment at GCSE level.

This activity offered fertile ground for the School of Education at the University of Bath to join forces with a team of science teachers drawn from a wide spectrum of educational experience, and with a major publisher to create a flexible curriculum model and then develop resources to fit it. This group addressed the task of satisfying these requirements:

- the new syllabus and examination demands of A- and AS-level courses;
- the provision of materials suitable for both the core and option parts of syllabuses;
- the striking of an appropriate balance of opportunities for students to acquire knowledge and understanding, develop skills and concepts, and to appreciate the applications and implications of science;
- the encouragement of a degree of independent learning through highly interactive texts;
- the satisfaction of the needs of a wide ability range of students at this level.

Some of these objectives were easier to achieve than others. Relationships to still evolving syllabuses demand the most rigorous analysis and a sense of vision – and optimism – regarding their eventual destination. Original assumptions about AS-level, for example, as a distinct though complementary sibling to A-level needed to be revised.

The Project, though, always regarded itself as more than a provider of materials, important as this is, and concerned itself equally with the process of provision – how material can best be written and shaped to meet the requirements of the educational market-place. This aim found expression in two principal forms: the idea of secondment at the University and the extensive trialling of early material in schools and colleges.

Most authors enjoyed a period of secondment from teaching, which not only allowed them to reflect and write more strategically (and, particularly so, in a supportive academic environment) but, equally, to engage with each other in wrestling with the issues in question.

The Project saw in the trialling a crucial test for the acceptance of its ideas and their execution. Over one hundred institutions and one thousand students participated, and responses were invited from teachers and students alike. The reactions generally confirmed the soundness of the model and allowed for more scrupulous textual housekeeping, as details of confusion, ambiguity or plain misunderstanding were revised and reordered.

The test of all teaching must be in the quality of the learning, and the proof of these resources will be in the understanding and ease of accessibility which they generate. The Project, ultimately, is both a collection of materials and a message of faith in the science curriculum of the future.

J. J. Thompson

How to use this book

In recent years electronics has been taught in schools through a systems approach which describes the function and use of a device without students having to understand the physics behind its operation. In this way, students can quickly produce a working solution to a design problem without the need to study electrical concepts and components. The reason for the systems approach is that technology is changing so rapidly that any knowledge about how a component works will soon be redundant as new components replace old ones, but the function of the component will remain the same. In response to this method of teaching electronics, a number of 'systems' kits have been manufactured which consist of many different types of input, process and output building blocks that can be connected together to build useful systems. Telecommunication and microprocessor systems can also be studied using commercial kits. Systems kits provide a useful tool for initial project development but the circuit must eventually be constructed using discrete components. For this reason, post-16 courses in electronics do not wholly adopt a systems approach: they require you to have a knowledge of the characteristics of various components as well as the fundamental concepts of electrical theory to enable you to select the most appropriate component. The authors have attempted to find a balance between the systems approach and the more traditional physics approach, with emphasis on what a component does rather than why it does it.

The book is divided into four themes. Theme 1 looks at the systems approach and basic theory necessary to design systems from discrete components. Theme 2, on digital systems, looks at the functions of logic gates and their application to logic and timing circuits. Theme 3 deals with the principles of amplification in analogue circuits and covers the fundamental concepts of radio systems. Finally, Theme 4 looks at microprocessor systems and the subsystems required to interface computers with the real world.

The book is geared to the requirements of students who are following an A-level or AS-level in physics and are taking the option in electronics, and also to students following an AS-level course in electronics. The syllabuses are quite diverse and it has not been possible to cover the content of each syllabus in detail. Owing to this diversity we advise you to look carefully at the subject content of your particular Examination Board, as some of the ideas met in this book may not be relevant to your particular syllabus. In addition, ask your Examination Board which symbols they are using. The ones in this book are those specified by the Association for Science Education (ASE).

Learning Objectives

Each chapter starts with a list of learning objectives, which outline what you should gain from the chapter and which often link closely to statements in a course syllabus. The objectives can help you make notes for revision.

Questions

In-text questions occur at the end of sections of the work which should consolidate what you have learned. Examination questions are included in Appendix C. Answers to the numerical parts of questions can be found in Appendix D.

Investigations

You cannot learn electronics by simply reading about it, so each chapter includes suggestions for practical work which can be carried out using discrete components available from the components suppliers suggested in Appendix E.

Margin Notes

These include information that may be anecdotal or interesting.

Summaries

Each chapter ends with a brief summary of its contents. These summaries together with the learning objectives should allow you to check your own progress.

Further reading and resources

Appendix E contains reference to magazines and software that may be useful for project development. The resources section gives details about suppliers of equipment.

Acknowledgements

The authors would like to express their thanks to David Black and his colleagues at Si-Plan Electronics Research, and to David Snashall and Ian Kemp for their help in writing this book.

The authors and publishers would like to thank the following for permission to reproduce copyright material:

The Institution of Electrical Engineers for material in section 4.9, page 45, which originally appeared in 'The Historical Background of Switches' in *Electronics Education*, Summer 1994.

The Consumers' Association for material in section 11.8, page 147, which originally appeared in *Which?* magazine in January 1996.

The Northern Examinations and Assessment Board, The Oxford and Cambridge Schools Examination Board, The University of Cambridge Local Examinations Syndicate and the University of London Examinations and Assessment Council for permission to reproduce examination questions in Appendix C of this book.

The authors and publishers would like to thank the following for permission to reproduce photographs and illustrations:

Alan Thomas: Theme 1 Introduction, page 1 (both); Figure 1.2(a), page 2; Figure 3.14, page 27; Figure 4.1, page 40; Figure 6.1, page 65; Figure 6.10, page 71; Figure 6.16(a), page 74; Figure 8.31, page 104; Figure 9.1, page 108
NASA/Science Photo Library: Theme 3 Introduction, page 87
Radio Spares: Figure 3.1(a to c), page 23; Figure 3.2(a), page 23; Figure 3.3(a), page 23; Figure 4.12, page 44; Figure 4.16, page 45; Figure 8.13(a and b), page 96; Figure 9.9, page 112; Figure 10.2, page 129
Panasonic: Figure 2.6, page 11
Physics Review, May 1995: Figure 4.6, page 42
Ferranti Electronics/A. Sternberg/Science Photo Library: Figure 3.28, page 35
Adam Hart-Davis/Science Photo Library: Figure 3.29(a and b), page 35
Mike McNamee/Science Photo Library: Figure 3.31, page 36
Air France: Figure 4.11, page 44
Maplin Electronics: Figure 4.17(a), page 46
Yamaha Musical Instruments: Theme 2 Introduction, page 49
Michael MacIntyre/Hutchison Picture Library: Theme 4 Introduction, page 127
Data Harvest plc: Figure 10.1, page 128; Figure 10.12, page 134
Unilab, Blackburn, England: Figure 11.5, page 143

Theme 1

BASIC ELECTRICITY AND COMPONENTS

Electronics as a field of engineering and applied physics has been around for about one hundred years but remained a matter for specialists and enthusiasts who pioneered such electronic systems as radio and television, telecommunications and computing. The invention of the transistor in 1948 and the subsequent development of miniaturised electronics has had a profound impact on most aspects of our lives.

A general understanding of the way electronic components and circuits function and the application of this knowledge to design 'systems' is fundamental to all branches of electronics. The method used to impart this information is called a 'systems approach' because it enables a satisfactory insight without having to learn every detail of each circuit, providing students with the opportunity to design and build simple electronic models of practical systems at an early stage. The systems approach coincides neatly with the fact that a large number of circuit functions are available 'ready made' as 'integrated circuits' which consist of basic circuits coupled together in a single block to perform a particular function. Integrated circuits are systems in themselves, but may also be joined together to perform more complex functions.

The computer illustrates the advancements in technology over the past decade or so. The typewriter and the word processor are examples of systems with the same input (the mechanical process of pressing the keys of the keyboard) and the same output (a printed document). The only difference between the two systems is how each system processes the information it receives.

The computer system illustrates how far technology has advanced from the manual typewriter of an earlier decade.

Chapter 1

SYSTEMS AND BASIC ELECTRICITY

LEARNING OBJECTIVES

After studying this chapter you should be able to:

1. understand what is meant by a systems approach to electronics;

2. define and use the terms 'potential difference', 'current', 'resistance' and 'conductance';

3. define and use the term 'power';

4. explain what is meant by d.c. and a.c.;

5. define and use the terms 'frequency', 'period', 'amplitude' and 'r.m.s. value'.

1.1 ELECTRONIC SYSTEMS

When electrical circuits are connected together to control output devices, the whole arrangement is called a **system**, with various **subsystems** or **building blocks** making up the complete system.

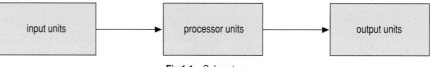

| input units | → | processor units | → | output units |

Fig 1.1 Subsystems.

Fig 1.1 shows how building blocks fit together to form a complete system. Complex electronic systems can be 'broken down' into subsystems to help understand the function of the complete system. Commercial kits, such as 'Unilab Alpha', are available which use the idea of a systems approach. Once you know what each subsystem does, it is relatively easy to assemble the blocks to produce a useful electronic system.

Fig 1.2 **(a)** Alpha kit modules joined together as in (b), with a bar magnet placed near the magnetic switch unit. **(b)** Block diagram of the system in (a).

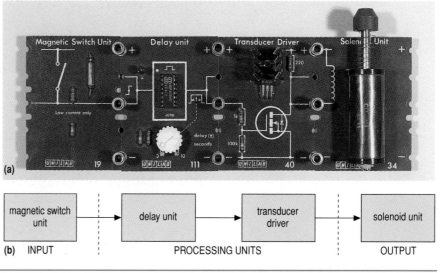

| magnetic switch unit | → | delay unit | → | transducer driver | → | solenoid unit |

(b) INPUT   PROCESSING UNITS   OUTPUT

Fig 1.2 shows how a 'Door entry' system can be constructed using Alpha kit modules. When a magnet (representing a magnetic strip on a plastic card) is passed over the switch unit, the delay unit operates the transducer driver but only for a set length of time. The transducer driver supplies sufficient current to energise the solenoid unit, which controls the door opening mechanism, such as a bolt.

INVESTIGATION

Designing various electronic systems

If you have kits available, use them to become familiar with the function of various subsystems. Try designing the following electronic system.

- Design a 'door-bell' for a deaf person.
  Specification: When the 'bell push' is pressed, a lamp flashes on and off.

Write your own specification for each of the following ideas and construct circuits using any suitable electronic kit. The specification should state what the system is intended to do.

- Intruder alarm
- Automatic porch light
- Automatic garden sprinkler which operates when the soil is dry
- Car courtesy light
- Event counter for a car entering a car park

The advantage of a **systems approach** is that you do not have to understand the complexities of how each subsystem works. You simply have to know what a particular block does, that is, each subsystem is treated as a **black box**.

Once you have devised a solution using, for example, an electronic kit, the next step is to construct each building block from discrete electronic components. Therefore you need to know what each component does and how to connect it to other components to make each block work properly. Connecting subsystems together is a more difficult task since the output from one circuit acts as the input to another circuit. **Interfacing devices** are sometimes required between two circuits to ensure that there is sufficient voltage and current transfer between them. In Fig 1.2 the solenoid requires a greater operating current than the delay unit can supply, so the transducer driver acts as a **current amplifying interface**.

Before you start to build your own electronic circuits, you need to have an understanding of basic electrical theory.

1.2 BASIC CONCEPTS

Electronics is largely concerned with the controlled movement or flow of electrons, and such movement occurs most easily in metallic materials which are said to have a low **resistance** (or high conductivity) and are classified as **conductors**. Materials which offer an extremely large opposition to electron flow are known as **insulators**.

When a **potential** (or **voltage**) **difference**, supplied by a battery for example, is applied across a conductor, it causes a **current** to pass through it. The electric current is a measure of the rate of flow of electrons (negatively charged particles) past any point in the circuit. The **charge** Q which flows past a point in time t if there is a constant current I, is given by the equation

$$\text{charge, } Q = \text{current, } I \times \text{time, } t \qquad Q = It$$

The unit of charge is the **coulomb**. One coulomb (1 C) is the charge that in one second (1 s) crosses a section of a circuit in which there is a current of one ampere (1 A).

The potential difference (p.d.) between two points in a circuit is defined as the electrical energy converted to other forms of energy when unit charge passes from one point to the other, i.e. the electrons dissipate energy as they pass through a resistive circuit. The unit of potential difference is the **volt**. One volt (1 V) is the potential difference between two points in a circuit when one **joule** of energy is converted when one coulomb passes from one point to the other. The equation for p.d. is:

$$\text{potential difference, } V = \frac{\text{energy converted, } E}{\text{charge, } Q}$$

$$V = \frac{E}{Q} \qquad Q = \frac{E}{V} \qquad E = VQ$$

1.3 RESISTANCE

The amount of current depends on the **electrical resistance** of the circuit.

The relationship between resistance, potential difference and current was formulated by Georg Simon Ohm in 1827 and is defined by the equation below:

$$\text{resistance, } R = \frac{\text{potential difference, } V}{\text{current, } I}$$

$$R = \frac{V}{I} \qquad I = \frac{V}{R} \qquad V = IR$$

Symbol notation for quantities and units
Symbols representing physical quantities are printed in italic, e.g. a voltage, V.
Roman (upright) capitals are used to represent the symbols for units, e.g. 3 volts is written as 3 V.

The unit of resistance is the ohm. The resistor has a resistance of one ohm (1 Ω) if there is a current of one ampere (1 A) through it when the potential difference (p.d.) across it is one volt (1 V). The currents associated with electronic circuits are usually small and it is useful to note that a conductor has a resistance of one kilohm (1 kΩ = 1000 Ω) if a current of one milliampere (1 mA = 0.001 A) passes through it when there is a potential difference of one volt across it.

A **resistor** is a component part much used in electronics which is manufactured to give a specific value of resistance.

The circuit in Fig 1.3 shows how the resistance of the resistor can be measured. The ammeter measures the current and is connected in series with the resistor. The voltmeter measures the potential difference and is connected directly across (in parallel with) the resistor.

A **multimeter** can be used to measure current, potential difference or resistance. The use of a multimeter is described in Appendix A.

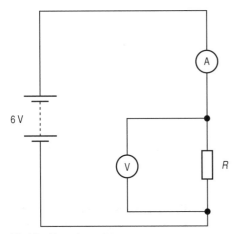

Fig 1.3 Measuring resistance.

QUESTION

1.1 How much current will pass through a resistance of 47 kΩ if the potential difference across it is 5 V?

If resistors are connected in series as in Fig 1.4(a) there is only one path for the current; therefore each resistor has the same current. If the resistors are connected in parallel as in Fig 1.4(b), there are two paths for the current from the battery. The charge in the circuit must be conserved so the total current entering the junction must equal the total current leaving the junction. This is a consequence of **Kirchhoff's first law** which states that:

The algebraic sum of the currents at a junction is zero.

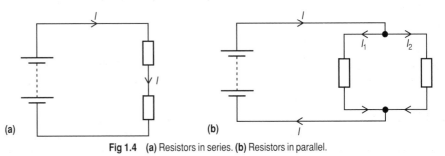

Fig 1.4 (a) Resistors in series. (b) Resistors in parallel.

SYSTEMS AND BASIC ELECTRICITY

The **electrical conductance** of a conductor (G) is a measure of the ability of a circuit to pass current when a p.d. is applied. The electrical conductance is the reciprocal of its resistance, i.e.

$$G = \frac{1}{R} \quad \text{or} \quad G = \frac{I}{V}$$

where the conductance G is measured in siemens (S) and resistance R is measured in ohms (Ω).

1.4 POWER

When there is a current through a circuit which has resistance, the energy expended causes the material to be heated. This effect is put to good use in a kettle element and the electrical power 'consumed' by the element and converted to thermal energy is measured in watts (W). Larger units of power which can be seen on domestic appliances are kilowatts (kW). Electronic power ratings are often in milliwatts (mW) (1 kW = 1000 W, 1000 mW = 1 W).

The rate at which electrical energy is converted to thermal energy in a resistor can be calculated using the following equation:

$$\text{power, } P = \frac{\text{energy converted, } E}{\text{time, } t} \quad P = \frac{E}{t}$$

where power is in watts (W), energy is in joules (J) and time is in seconds (s).

Using the earlier equations, $E = VQ$, $I = V/R$ and $I = Q/t$, it can be seen that

$$P = \frac{VQ}{t} = VI = IRI = I^2R \quad \text{or} \quad P = VI = V\frac{V}{R} = \frac{V^2}{R}$$

The three important formulae for power are:

$$P = VI \qquad P = I^2R \qquad P = \frac{V^2}{R}$$

where power is in watts, current is in amperes, resistance is in ohms and p.d. is in volts.

1.5 POWER SUPPLIES

The current supplied by a battery is called **direct current (d.c.)**. A direct current flows in one direction only which, by convention, is said to flow from the positive (+) terminal of the battery to the negative (−) terminal. (Electron flow is in fact from negative to positive.)

The **electromotive force (e.m.f.)** of a battery is measured as the p.d. across its terminals when it is not supplying a current. When a battery drives a current round a circuit some of the electrical energy is converted into thermal energy in the battery due to its **internal resistance**. For this reason, the terminal p.d. is always less than the e.m.f. of the battery. The circuit in Fig 1.5 consists of a battery of e.m.f. E and internal resistance r, connected to a resistor of resistance R.

The e.m.f. of the battery = p.d. across r + p.d. across R, i.e.

$$E = Ir + IR$$

where IR is the terminal p.d. of the battery. This is an example of **Kirchhoff's second law** which states that:

Round any closed circuit the algebraic sum of voltages is zero.

If therefore a charge moves around the circuit but returns to the original point, any gains of electrical energy it might have had in its journey must be balanced by corresponding losses of energy.

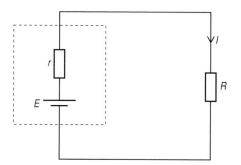

Fig 1.5 Internal resistance and e.m.f.

Batteries
Zinc–carbon cells (the typical torch cell) have a higher internal resistance than alkaline cells. This means that a 1.5 V alkaline cell will deliver a larger current to a load resistor than a 1.5 V zinc–carbon cell.

QUESTION

1.2 If a cell, with e.m.f. 1.50 V and internal resistance 0.5 Ω, is used to supply a current of 100 mA, calculate the terminal p.d. of the cell.

Electrical generators which supply the 'mains' current produce **alternating current (a.c.)**. The moving electrons travel one way in the conductor during a 'half-cycle' of the supply and the other way for the other half-cycle. Mains a.c. has a **sinusoidal** (sine wave) variation and the shape of the waveform is shown in Fig 1.6.

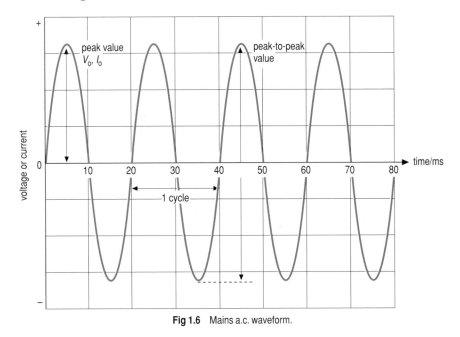

Fig 1.6 Mains a.c. waveform.

The **frequency** of the mains supply in the UK is 50 Hz. This means that 50 complete waves are generated in one second. The time for one cycle is called the **period** of the wave:

$$\text{frequency, } f = \frac{1}{\text{period, } T} \qquad f = \frac{1}{T}$$

where f is in hertz (Hz) and T is in seconds (s).

QUESTION

1.3 If the time taken for a sinusoidal voltage to rise from zero to its peak value is 5 ms, what is its frequency?

The **amplitude** or peak value of the sine wave is its maximum positive or negative value. It is equal to half the peak-to-peak value of the sine wave.

When alternating current or direct current is passed through a resistor, electrical energy is dissipated as heat in the resistor. Since alternating current (and voltage) continuously changes in magnitude, an effective value is assigned to it which would produce the same heat energy in the resistor as a direct current (or voltage) of the same value. This effective value of alternating current (or voltage) is called the **root mean square** (r.m.s.) current (or voltage). In the UK the mains r.m.s. voltage is 230 V, which means that this a.c. voltage gives the same heating effect as a d.c. voltage of 230 V.

It can be shown that for a sine wave

$$\text{r.m.s. value} = \frac{\text{peak value}}{\sqrt{2}} \approx 0.7 \times \text{peak value}$$

$$V_{\text{rms}} = \frac{V_0}{\sqrt{2}} \qquad I_{\text{rms}} = \frac{I_0}{\sqrt{2}}$$

where V_0 and I_0 are the peak voltage and current values respectively.

SYSTEMS AND BASIC ELECTRICITY

1.4 Calculate the peak voltage of the 230 V mains supply.

1.5 An alternating voltage of peak value 34 V operates a low-voltage soldering iron. What battery voltage would provide the same heating power?

The power P of an a.c. device is given by the same expression as for d.c. since a 6 W light bulb, for example, produces the same light from a 12 V d.c. supply as from a 12 V a.c. supply because the 12 V a.c. refers to its r.m.s. value:

$$P = I_{rms}V_{rms} \quad \text{so} \quad P = \frac{I_0}{\sqrt{2}}\frac{V_0}{\sqrt{2}} = \frac{I_0V_0}{2}$$

Most electronic systems require a steady low-voltage d.c. supply. Batteries are suitable for low-current portable equipment but many circuits are operated from a power supply unit connected to the a.c. mains. A power supply unit consists of a transformer to transform the 230 V to a lower voltage, e.g. 12 V, a bridge rectifier to convert a.c. to d.c., a smoothing capacitor to produce a steady d.c. and a voltage regulator to stabilise the d.c. output. You will learn more about the components of a power supply unit in subsequent chapters.

QUESTION

1.6 The power of an electric kettle is 3 kW. Calculate the r.m.s. current if the mains voltage is 230 V.

SUMMARY

Electronic subsystems fit together in the following basic pattern:

Input units → Processor units → Output units

Resistance, $R = \dfrac{\text{potential difference, } V}{\text{current, } I}$

Charge, $Q = I \times t$

Potential difference, $V = \dfrac{E}{Q}$

Electrical conductance, $G = \dfrac{1}{R}$ or $G = \dfrac{I}{V}$

Power, $P = I^2R$ or $P = \dfrac{V^2}{R}$

In a.c. theory:

$$V_{rms} = \frac{V_0}{\sqrt{2}} \qquad I_{rms} = \frac{I_0}{\sqrt{2}}$$

$$P = I_{rms}V_{rms} = \frac{I_0V_0}{2}$$

Chapter 2

PASSIVE COMPONENTS

LEARNING OBJECTIVES

After studying this chapter you should be able to:

1. identify resistors and understand what is meant by tolerance, power rating and preferred values;

2. calculate the effective resistance of resistors in series and in parallel;

3. calculate the effective capacitance of capacitors in series and in parallel;

4. describe the exponential growth and decay curves for capacitor and inductor circuits;

5. understand the terms 'impedance' and 'reactance' when applied to capacitors, inductors and resistors in a.c. circuits;

6. use phasor diagrams to calculate the vector sum of the voltages in *LCR* a.c. circuits.

Components are the building blocks of electronic systems and, before you can start to construct circuits, you need to know certain things about them. For this purpose, we are not concerned with how they work, but we need to know how to use them. This chapter is concerned with three of the most common components used in subsystems, namely, **resistors**, **capacitors** and **inductors**. They are often referred to as **passive** components as they cannot, by themselves, generate a voltage or current.

2.1 COMPONENT DATA

Information about components can be obtained from electronic catalogues such as Farnell Electronic Components, RS, Rapid Electronics and Maplin. The RS catalogue is also available on compact disc for a CD ROM computer system.

Data sheets can also be obtained, from the component suppliers, which give details of a component's specification.

2.2 RESISTORS

Resistors are used widely in electronic circuits to limit the current flowing through devices and to provide a potential difference.

Table 2.1 Resistor bands

Band 1	The first number in the value
Band 2	The second number in the value
Band 3	The number of noughts which follow the second number
Band 4	Tolerance

Identifying resistors

Standard moulded carbon film resistors are marked with four colour bands so that their values can be read easily (see Table 2.1). The bands are positioned towards one end of the resistor so that it is easy to identify which is the first band in the code. Fig 2.1 illustrates the use of the four-band colour code.

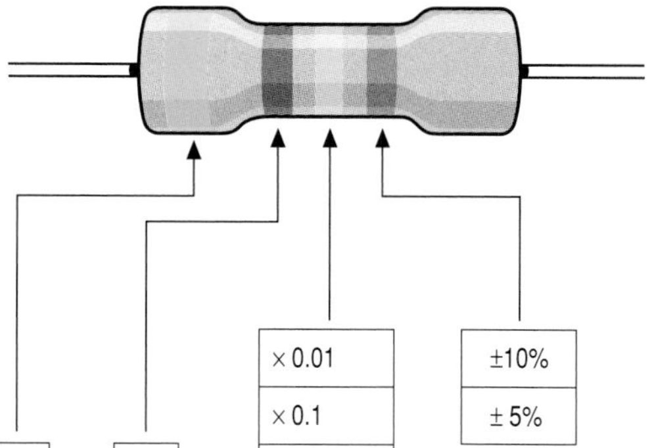

Table 2.2   Printed code

Code	Value
1R2	$1.2\,\Omega$
12R	$12\,\Omega$
120R	$120\,\Omega$
1K2	$1.2\,k\Omega$
12K	$12\,k\Omega$
120K	$120\,k\Omega$
1M2	$1.2\,M\Omega$
12M	$12\,M\Omega$

Tolerance:
F = ±1%
G = ±2%
J = ±5%
K = ±10%
M = ±20%

Table 2.3   Preferred values

E24 series (±5%) – gold band	E12 series (±10%) – silver band
10	10
11	
12	12
13	
15	15
16	
18	18
20	
22	22
24	
27	27
30	
33	33
36	
39	39
43	
47	47
51	
56	56
62	
68	68
75	
82	82
91	

Fig 2.1   Resistor four-band colour code.

More expensive metal film resistors which are more accurate are often marked with five colour bands. The first three bands give numbers, the fourth band gives the number of noughts and the fifth the tolerance (brown ±1%, red ±2%).

Another code that is sometimes used for marking resistors is the BS 1852 code. The code is often used for printing resistance values on circuit diagrams. Table 2.2 illustrates how this code works.

Tolerance

Inaccuracies occur in the manufacture of resistors, which means that there will be some deviation of the actual value from the intended resistance value. The acceptable range in the value is called the **tolerance**. For example, a $330\,\Omega$ resistance with a tolerance of ±10% (orange orange brown silver) would have a value between $297\,\Omega$ and $363\,\Omega$. To avoid overlap of resistor values due to tolerance, manufacturers only produce resistors with **preferred values**. The preferred values depend on the tolerance, and a greater accuracy of manufacture (lower tolerance) means that more resistor values are produced because the overlap will not be so great. Preferred values are grouped into series, as shown in Table 2.3.

Power rating

When selecting a resistor, its **power rating** as well as its value and tolerance should be checked. The power rating tells you how much energy can be dissipated without damaging the resistor.

Example: A resistor is needed to allow a current of 20 mA to pass when the potential difference across it is 12 V. To select the resistor you need, perform the following calculation:

$$R = \frac{V}{I} = \frac{12\,V}{0.02\,A} = 600\,\Omega \quad \text{so} \quad P = IV = 0.02\,A \times 12\,V = 0.24\,W$$

Therefore, select a resistor of $620\,\Omega$ (assuming E24 series available) with a power rating of 0.5 W. (It is **not** good practice to work at the extremes of the power rating; always use a rating value which is at least one-and-a-half times greater than the calculated dissipation.)

Usual power ratings are 0.125 W, 0.25 W, 0.5 W, 1.0 W, 2.0 W and 2.5 W. The physical size of the resistor is usually an indication of its power rating; the larger the power rating, the larger the physical size of the resistor.

QUESTIONS

2.1 What are the colour codes of these resistors?
(a) $3.3\,M\Omega \pm 10\%$ (b) $15.0\,k\Omega \pm 1\%$

2.2 What are the printed codes of these resistors?
(a) $100\,\Omega \pm 5\%$ (b) $5.6\,k\Omega \pm 10\%$

2.3 A resistor of $100\,\Omega$ with a power rating of 0.25 W is used in a circuit. Is it safe to pass a current of 60 mA through this resistor?

2.3 RESISTOR NETWORKS

The lower the tolerance of a resistor, the more expensive it is and, for this reason, the E12 series is commonly used. There are only 12 preferred values in this series but it is possible to combine resistors to give other values not in this series.

Resistors in series

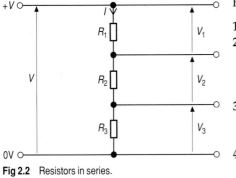

Fig 2.2 Resistors in series.

Rules for series circuits (Fig 2.2):

1. The same current I flows through each resistor.
2. The sum of the p.d.'s across each resistor is equal to the p.d. across the combination,

$$V = V_1 + V_2 + V_3$$

3. The total resistance R of resistors in series is equal to their sum,

$$R = R_1 + R_2 + R_3$$

4. The total resistance is greater than the largest resistance in the series network.

QUESTION

2.4 What single resistor is equivalent to two $3.3\,k\Omega$ connected in series? What is the nearest preferred value (E12 series) to this resistor?

Resistors in parallel

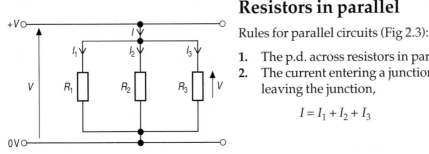

Fig 2.3 Resistors in parallel.

Rules for parallel circuits (Fig 2.3):

1. The p.d. across resistors in parallel is the same.
2. The current entering a junction is equal to the sum of the currents leaving the junction,

$$I = I_1 + I_2 + I_3$$

PASSIVE COMPONENTS

3. The total resistance R of resistors in parallel can be calculated from the equation

$$\frac{1}{R} = \frac{1}{R_1} + \frac{1}{R_2} + \frac{1}{R_3}$$

4. The total resistance is less than the smallest resistance in the parallel network.

QUESTIONS

2.5 What is the equivalent resistor for a 470 Ω and 80 Ω resistor connected in parallel?

2.6 What is the total resistance of the resistor network shown in Fig 2.4?

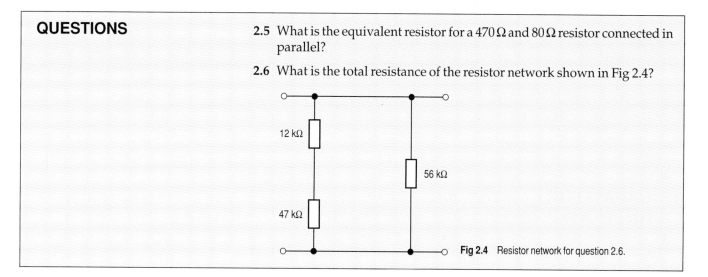

12 kΩ

56 kΩ

47 kΩ

Fig 2.4 Resistor network for question 2.6.

2.4 CAPACITORS

(a)

(b)

Fig 2.5 Capacitor types: **(a)** polarised and **(b)** unpolarised.

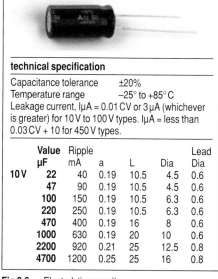

technical specification

Capacitance tolerance	±20%
Temperature range	−25° to +85° C

Leakage current, IµA = 0.01 CV or 3µA (whichever is greater) for 10 V to 100 V types. IµA = less than 0.03 CV + 10 for 450 V types.

	Value µF	Ripple mA	a	L	Dia	Lead Dia
10 V	22	40	0.19	10.5	4.5	0.6
	47	90	0.19	10.5	4.5	0.6
	100	150	0.19	10.5	6.3	0.6
	220	250	0.19	10.5	6.3	0.6
	470	400	0.19	16	8	0.6
	1000	630	0.19	20	10	0.6
	2200	920	0.21	25	12.5	0.8
	4700	1200	0.25	25	16	0.8

Fig 2.6 Electrolytic capacitor.

A capacitor can store electrical charge and therefore energy. Its ability to store charge is called its **capacitance** and is measured in farads (F). The amount of charge a capacitor can store depends on its capacitance and the p.d. across it. The p.d. across the capacitor, V, is directly proportional to the charge, Q, on the capacitor:

charge, Q = capacitance, C × potential difference, V

$$Q = CV \qquad C = \frac{Q}{V} \qquad V = \frac{Q}{C}$$

where charge is measured in coulombs (C), capacitance in farads (F) and p.d. in volts (V).

One farad is a very large unit of capacitance and capacitors of this size are generally only used for applications which require memory retention under power failure conditions such as in microcomputers. Smaller capacitor values are used in most electronic circuits. Common values are the microfarad (µF), nanofarad (nF) and picofarad (pF).

$$1\,\mu F = 10^{-6}\,F \qquad 1\,nF = 10^{-9}\,F \qquad 1\,pF = 10^{-12}\,F$$

A glance through the capacitors section of any components catalogue will demonstrate the numerous types of capacitor available.

There are basically two types of capacitor, **polarised** and **unpolarised.** Their symbols are shown in Fig 2.5. Electrolytic (which include **tantalum**) capacitors are polarised and must be connected the correct way round.

Fig 2.6 shows an electrolytic capacitor. In order to select the most appropriate capacitor for a particular purpose, an understanding of its technical specification is required.

Working voltage is the maximum voltage that should be applied across a capacitor without damaging it. **Polypropylene** capacitors are used for high-voltage circuits up to 1500 V d.c. (This is the peak-to-peak voltage not the r.m.s. voltage for a.c. circuits.)

Capacitors basically consist of two metal plates separated by an insulating material (the **dielectric**) through which there should not be any current. However, because a perfect insulator does not exist, there will always be a small **leakage current**. The smaller the leakage current, the better the capacitor. Electrolytic capacitors have a large leakage current. **Ceramic** capacitors have a small leakage current.

Capacitance is affected by change of temperature. The capacitance remains within the tolerance limits for the **temperature range** given. **Polycarbonate** capacitors offer high stability with temperature whereas **polyester** types are less stable but cost slightly less.

Values of capacitance vary even for capacitors manufactured in the same way. **Tolerance** refers to the acceptable range above and below the stated capacitance. Tolerance can be as high as ±50% (**electrolytic** capacitors) and, because of this, only a few values are manufactured such as multiples of 1.0, 2.2 and 4.7. Electrolytic capacitors can be manufactured with higher capacitances than any other type of capacitor.

Smaller capacitance capacitors are manufactured with tolerances as low as ±1% (**polystyrene** and **silvered mica** capacitors) and more values are available (1.0, 1.2, 1.5, 1.8, 2.2, 2.7, 3.3, 3.9, 4.7, 5.6, 6.8 and 8.2) in these types.

2.5 CAPACITOR NETWORKS

It is possible to combine capacitors to give other values which are not manufactured, but theoretical values may be very different from the actual values obtained due to the tolerance of capacitors.

Capacitors in series

Rules for series circuits (Fig 2.7):

Fig 2.7 Capacitors in series.

1. The effective capacitance C of capacitors connected in series can be calculated from the equation

$$\frac{1}{C} = \frac{1}{C_1} + \frac{1}{C_2} + \frac{1}{C_3}$$

2. The effective capacitance is less than the smallest capacitance in the series network.

Capacitors in parallel

Rules for parallel circuits (Fig 2.8):

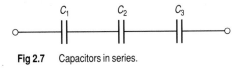

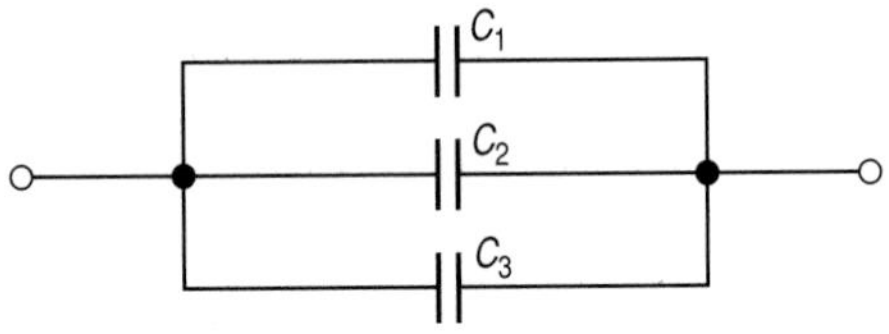

Fig 2.8 Capacitors in parallel.

1. The effective capacitance C of capacitors connected in parallel can be calculated from the equation

$$C = C_1 + C_2 + C_3$$

2. The effective capacitance is greater than the largest capacitance in the parallel network.

QUESTIONS

2.7 A polyester capacitor has a capacitance of 0.47 μF and a tolerance of ±10%. What are the maximum and minimum values it can have?

2.8 An electrolytic 'memory back-up' capacitor of 0.33 F has a tolerance of −20% to +80%. What are the maximum and minimum values it can have?

2.9 A 0.33 μF and a 0.47 μF are connected in series. What is the equivalent capacitance?

2.10 What is the combined capacitance of the capacitors in (a) Fig 2.7 and (b) Fig 2.8 when $C_1 = 10$ μF, $C_2 = 1$ μF and $C_3 = 4.7$ μF?

PASSIVE COMPONENTS

2.6 CHARGING A CAPACITOR

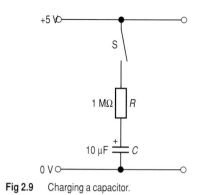

Fig 2.9   Charging a capacitor.

Calculating the rate at which the capacitor charges through a resistor

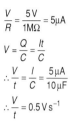

$$\frac{V}{R} = \frac{5\,V}{1M\Omega} = 5\mu A$$

$$V = \frac{Q}{C} = \frac{It}{C}$$

$$\therefore \frac{V}{t} = \frac{I}{C} = \frac{5\mu A}{10\mu F}$$

$$\therefore \frac{V}{t} = 0.5\,V\,s^{-1}$$

A capacitor can be charged by connecting a power supply across it. The rate at which the capacitor charges up can be controlled by connecting a resistor in series with the capacitor as in Fig 2.9. At the instant the switch S is closed, the capacitor will be uncharged and the total circuit resistance will be due to resistor R. The initial current will be $5\mu A$. If a uniform charging rate was maintained the p.d. across the capacitor would rise at a rate of 0.5 V per second. It would take 10 seconds for the p.d. across the capacitor to rise from 0 V to 5 V. The solid straight line graph in Fig 2.10 shows how the voltage across the capacitor rises with time if this initial rate of charging was maintained. However, the initial rate of charging cannot be maintained since the p.d. across the capacitor opposes the supply voltage and therefore limits the charging current to a value below $5\mu A$. Consider the instant when $t = 1\,s$. From the graph in Fig 2.10 we can see that the p.d. across the capacitor has risen to 0.5 V, which opposes the 5 V of the supply, leaving 4.5 V to continue the charging of the capacitor. The charging current will therefore be $4.5\mu A$ and the rate of increase of voltage would be $0.45\,Vs^{-1}$. Since a rise in voltage of a further 4.5 V is needed before C is completely charged, the time required to do this, if this new rate of charging was maintained, would still be 10 s. At the instant $t = 4\,s$ the p.d. across C has risen to 1.6 V, leaving 3.4 V to continue charging the capacitor. The charging current is $3.4\mu A$ and therefore C still requires a further 10 s to be fully charged. At $t = 8\,s$ the p.d. across C has risen to 2.8 V, leaving 2.2 V to continue charging the capacitor. The charging current is now $2.2\mu A$ and C still requires a further 10 s to be fully charged. The dashed straight lines on the graph illustrate these new constant rates. As a result of the charging current getting smaller and smaller, the charge on the plates of the capacitor does not accumulate as quickly and the p.d. across the capacitor rises less and less rapidly. In theory the capacitor can never be completely charged. The actual shape of the charging curve is known as an **exponential** curve and is shown in Fig 2.10.

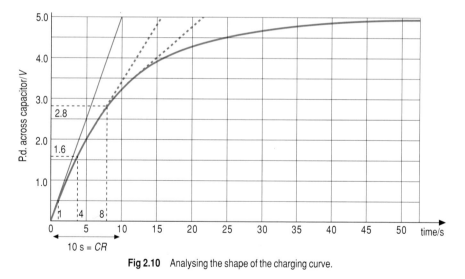

Fig 2.10   Analysing the shape of the charging curve.

The rate of growth of voltage with time depends upon the value of the capacitance and resistance. The main feature of the graph is the **time constant** defined as the **product of the capacitance and resistance, CR**:

time constant, t = capacitance, C × resistance, R

$$t = CR$$

where t is in seconds (s), C is in farads (F) and R is in ohms (Ω).

QUESTION

2.11   What is the time constant of a $10\,\mu F$ capacitor in series with a $470\,k\Omega$ resistor?

The time constant for the circuit in Fig 2.9 is 10 s ($10^6\,\Omega \times 10 \times 10^{-6}\,$F), which was the time required for the capacitor to become fully charged if the initial rate of charging was maintained. It can be shown that **in a time equal to CR seconds the p.d. across the capacitor rises to 63% of the supply voltage.**

QUESTION

2.12 If the combination of C and R in question 2.11 is connected to a 9 V d.c. source, what will be the p.d. across the capacitor after 4.7 s?

Natural logarithms
Scientific calculators have the facility to find the term e^x. Calculate the index x, i.e. $-t/CR$, and then use the e^x button on your calculator to give you the term $e^{-t/CR}$. If the power is unknown, take natural logarithms of both sides of the equation. Remember that, since the index is the logarithm, then

$$\ln e^{-t/CR} = -\frac{t}{CR}$$

The mathematics for proving that, in a time equal to CR seconds, the capacitor voltage rises to 0.63 of the final voltage is given in the box. (The proof is not required by all syllabuses.)

> The p.d. across the charging capacitor varies with time according to the relationship:
>
> $$V = V_0(1 - e^{-t/CR})$$
>
> where V is the p.d. across the capacitor after t seconds, C is the capacitance in farads (F), R is the resistance of the resistor in ohms (Ω) and V_0 is the supply voltage across the CR network. When $t = CR$
>
> $$V = V_0\left(1 - e^{-1}\right)$$
> $$= V_0\left(1 - \frac{1}{e}\right)$$
> $$= 0.632V_0$$
>
> i.e. 63% of the supply voltage. Here e is the exponential function, which has a value of 2.718.

Example: An initially uncharged capacitor of 10 µF is charged from a 6 V d.c. supply via a 2.2 MΩ resistor. Determine the p.d. across the capacitor 1 second after connecting the supply.
$C = 10\,\mu$F, $R = 2.2\,$MΩ, so $CR = 22\,$s. Then the equation

$$V = V_0(1 - e^{-t/CR})$$

gives, when $t = 1\,$s,

$$V = 6(1 - e^{-1/22}) = 0.27\,\text{V}$$

QUESTION

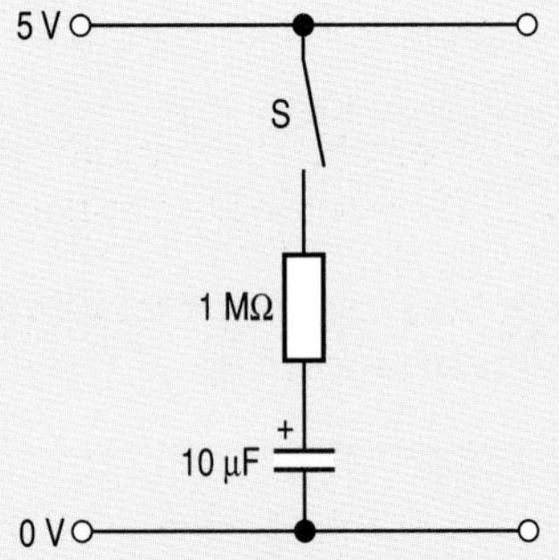

Fig 2.11 *CR* network for question 2.13.

2.13 (a) Calculate the time constant for the CR network in Fig 2.11.
(b) What is the p.d. across the capacitor after a time equal to one time constant?

(c) What is the p.d. across the capacitor 6 seconds after the switch S is closed?

Theoretically the p.d. across the capacitor never quite reaches the same value as the supply voltage, but a capacitor can be said to be fully charged after a time of five time constants, $5CR$. The p.d. across the capacitor is then within 1% of its final value and it is usual to take this period as the time in which the charge is completed.

2.7 DISCHARGING A CAPACITOR

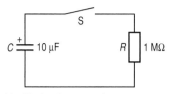

Fig 2.12 Discharging a capacitor.

If a charged capacitor is connected across a resistor (Fig 2.12), charge flows through the resistor until the capacitor is discharged. The initial discharge current is $5\,\mu A$ and at this instant the rate of fall of the p.d. across the capacitor is a maximum. The p.d. across the capacitor decreases exponentially with time, as shown in Fig 2.13.

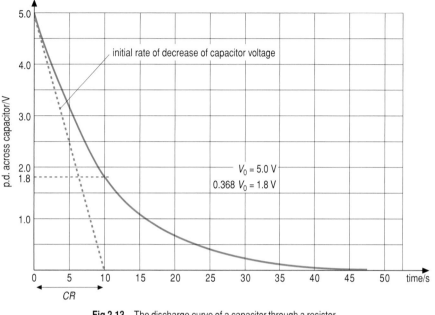

Fig 2.13   The discharge curve of a capacitor through a resistor.

Capacitor safety warning
A charged capacitor can deliver an electric shock, even when equipment has been switched off, similar to that which would have occurred had the victim directly touched the supply terminals. In commercial equipment, a high-value resistor is often connected across capacitors so that when the appliance is switched off the capacitor gradually discharges.

Again, the main feature of the decay curve is the time constant which is **the time it takes for the p.d. across the capacitor to fall to 37% of the supply voltage.**

The equation for this decay is:
$$V = V_0 e^{-t/CR}$$
If the capacitor is discharged for a time equal to the time constant CR then
$$V = V_0 e^{-CR/CR} = V_0 e^{-1} = 0.368 V_0$$
i.e. 37% of the initial voltage.

Example: A $47\,\mu F$ capacitor is charged to a p.d. of 9 V. The capacitor is then removed from the supply and connected to a $1\,M\Omega$ resistor. Determine the p.d. across the capacitor 1 minute later.
$C = 47\,\mu F$, $R = 1\,M\Omega$, so $CR = 47$ s. Then the equation $V = V_0 e^{-t/CR}$ gives, when $t = 60$ s, $V = 9e^{-60/47} = 2.51$ V.

QUESTIONS

2.14 A resistor is connected across a charged capacitor, the time constant of the circuit being 3.0 s. Calculate the fraction of initial charge stored which remains 1.0 s after the connection is made.

2.15 A fully charged $2200\,\mu F$ capacitor is discharged through a $180\,k\Omega$ resistor. Calculate the time constant for the circuit.

2.8 ENERGY STORAGE IN A CAPACITOR

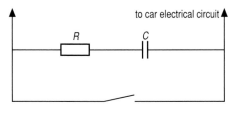

Fig 2.14   Car ignition switch.

When a capacitor is charged, it stores energy in the form of the electric field between the plates. The charge stored is proportional to the p.d. across the plates of the capacitor. It can be shown that

$$\text{energy stored,} \quad E = \tfrac{1}{2} \times \text{charge}, Q \times \text{potential difference,} \ V$$
$$E = \tfrac{1}{2}QV \quad \text{and} \quad E = \tfrac{1}{2}CV^2$$

where energy is measured in joules (J), charge in coulombs (C), capacitance in farads (F) and p.d. in volts (V).

When a capacitor is discharged, the energy is returned to the circuit, where it may be dissipated as heat.

QUESTION

2.16 A capacitor of 470 µF is charged from a 12 V supply. Determine the energy stored in the capacitor.

2.9 INDUCTORS

Fig 2.15   Inductor symbols: **(a)** air-core inductor; **(b)** iron-core inductor.

The third major type of passive component is the **inductor**. In its simplest form, an inductor is a coil of wire wound on an air or ferromagnetic (iron) core. The symbols for an inductor are shown in Fig 2.15. When an inductor is connected to a battery, the current in the coil sets up a magnetic field in the core. The appearance of the magnetic field inside the core causes an induced current to pass in the coil which opposes the current due to the battery. The property of an inductor that opposes changes in the current passing through it is called its **self-inductance** and is defined as

$$\text{self-inductance} = -\frac{\text{induced voltage}}{\text{rate of change of current}} \qquad L = -\frac{V}{\text{d}I/\text{d}t}$$

The unit of self-inductance is the **henry** (H). A coil is said to have a self-inductance of 1 H if an e.m.f. of 1 V is induced across it when the current through it is changing at a rate of $1\,\text{A s}^{-1}$. The minus sign is required because the direction of the back e.m.f. opposes the current direction.

In practice, a coil has both inductance and resistance. A pure inductor would have zero resistance. In practice, most inductors have a very small resistance which can often be ignored in calculations.

2.10 INDUCTORS IN D.C. CIRCUITS

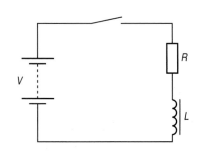

Fig 2.16   An *LR* circuit.

Consider the *LR* circuit in Fig 2.16 where a pure inductor is connected in series with a resistor and a d.c. battery of e.m.f. *V*. When the switch is closed the change in magnetic flux resulting from the appearance of current creates an induced e.m.f. across the coil which opposes the applied p.d. from the battery thereby preventing the current in the circuit rising instantaneously. The rate at which the current rises to a steady value is determined by the ratio of inductance to resistance and is known as the **time constant**:

$$\text{time constant,} \ t = \frac{L}{R}$$

The time constant L/R is the time it takes for the current to rise to 63% of its steady value or the time it takes for the current to fall to 37% of its initial steady value.

The mathematics for proving this is given in the box. (The proof is not required by all syllabuses.)

When the switch (in Fig 2.16) is closed, the current in the circuit takes time to build up to a steady value due to the opposition from the back e.m.f. induced in the coil. Suppose that at time t the current in the circuit is I. The battery e.m.f. is given by

battery e.m.f. = p.d. across resistor + p.d. across inductor

$$V = V_R + V_L$$

$$V = IR + L\frac{dI}{dt} \tag{1}$$

where R is the resistance of the circuit, which is in fact equal to the resistance of the resistor if L is a pure inductor with zero resistance.

It can be shown that the growth of current when the switch is first closed is exponential and the solution to equation (1) is given by

$$I = \frac{V}{R}\left(1 - e^{-Rt/L}\right) \tag{2}$$

When the current has already reached its steady value and the switch is then opened, the current decay is exponential and the solution to equation (1) is given by

$$I = \frac{V}{R}e^{-Rt/L} \tag{3}$$

The growth and decay of the current in the LR circuit is shown in Fig 2.17.

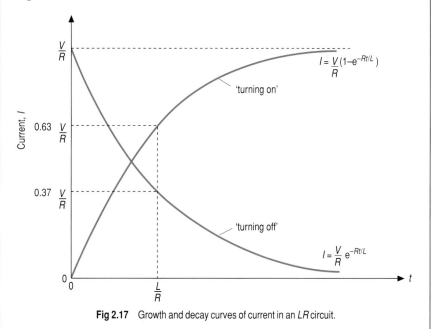

Fig 2.17 Growth and decay curves of current in an LR circuit.

From equation (2), if $t = L/R$ then

$$I = \frac{V}{R}\left(1 - e^{-1}\right) = 0.632\frac{V}{R}$$

From equation (3), if $t = L/R$ then

$$I = \frac{V}{R}e^{-1} = 0.368\frac{V}{R}$$

where V/R is the steady current that would flow through the resistor if there was no inductor in the circuit.

When alternating voltages are applied to capacitors or inductors, the magnitude of the current in the circuit depends not only on the capacitance and inductance but also on the frequency of the alternating supply, unlike a conventional resistor where the magnitude of the current is independent of the frequency.

Capacitive reactance

The resistance which a capacitor offers to a.c. is called its **capacitive reactance** X_C and is measured in ohms.

Capacitive reactance can be determined from the following equations:

$$X_C = \frac{V_{rms}}{I_{rms}} = \frac{V_0}{I_0}$$

It can also be shown that

$$X_C = \frac{1}{2\pi f C}$$

where C is the capacitance in farads and f is the frequency of the a.c. in hertz. When the frequency is zero the reactance is infinite, so no current can pass through the capacitor. This is what you would expect because when $f = 0$ the current is direct and, after the initial charging current, no current passes through the circuit.

QUESTION

2.17 Calculate the capacitive reactance of a capacitor with a capacitance of 47 µF if the frequency of the a.c. is **(a)** 5 Hz and **(b)** 50 Hz.

Fig 2.18 shows how X_C varies with frequency for a capacitor in an a.c. circuit.

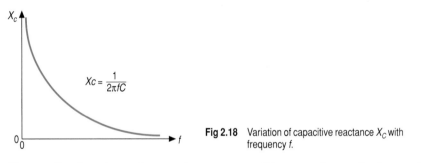

Fig 2.18 Variation of capacitive reactance X_C with frequency f.

For a fixed value of capacitance, capacitive reactance is inversely proportional to the frequency of the applied voltage. At low frequencies a capacitor acts like a high-value resistance, blocking the passage of low-frequency signals. At high frequencies, it acts like a low-value resistance, allowing high-frequency signals to pass easily.

Inductive reactance

The opposition which an inductor has to a.c. is called its **inductive reactance** X_L and is measured in ohms.

Inductive reactance can be determined from the following equations:

$$X_L = \frac{V_{rms}}{I_{rms}} = \frac{V_0}{I_0}$$

It can also be shown that

$$X_L = 2\pi f L$$

where L is the self-inductance of the inductor in henries and f is the frequency of the a.c. in hertz.

QUESTION

2.18 Calculate the inductive reactance of a coil with self-inductance of $0.5\,H$ if the frequency of the a.c. is **(a)** $5\,Hz$ and **(b)** $50\,Hz$.

Fig 2.19 shows how X_L varies with frequency for an inductor in an a.c. circuit.

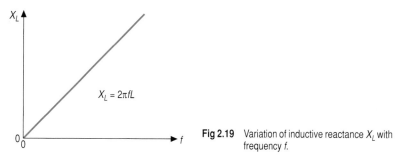

Fig 2.19 Variation of inductive reactance X_L with frequency f.

For a fixed value of inductance, inductive reactance is directly proportional to the frequency of the applied voltage. At low frequencies an inductor acts like a low-value resistance allowing low-frequency signals to pass easily. At high frequencies, it acts like a high-value resistance, blocking the passage of high-frequency signals.

Phase shift

The graphs in Fig 2.20 show how the current in a component and p.d. across a component vary for resistors, capacitors and inductors in a.c. circuits.

CIVIL
The acronym CIVIL can help you remember the phase shifts for inductors and capacitors. For a capacitive circuit (C), current leads voltage (I before V). Voltage leads current (V before I) for an inductive circuit (L).

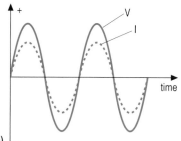

Fig 2.20 **(a)** Resistor in an a.c. circuit: I and V are in phase in a purely resistive circuit. **(b)** Capacitor in an a.c. circuit: I leads V by $90°$ in a purely capacitive circuit. **(c)** Inductor in an a.c. circuit: I lags V by $90°$ in a purely inductive circuit.

Ideal and practical *LC* circuits
Ideal inductors have zero resistance. Ideal capacitors have zero inductance and zero resistance. Practical capacitors have inductance and resistance and practical inductors have resistance. The combined effect of resistance and reactance is called impedance Z. Reactance and resistance of inductors can be treated as separate components in calculations.

For a resistor in an a.c. circuit, the current and p.d. reach their peak values at the same time. They are said to be in phase. In a pure capacitive circuit, there is a phase shift of $90°$ ($\pi/2$ radians), with the current leading the voltage by one quarter of a cycle. This is because the rate of charge flow (current) is maximum when the charge on the capacitor (and p.d. across the capacitor) is zero, i.e. when the capacitor is uncharged. Whenever the charge is a maximum the current in the circuit must at that instant be zero. The voltage across a pure inductive reactance and the current differ in phase by an angle of $90°$ (the voltage leads the current).

The phase relationship between voltage and current for inductors and capacitors in a.c. circuits can be illustrated as phasor diagrams as in Fig 2.21.

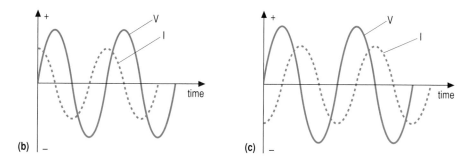

Fig 2.21 **(a)** Phasor diagram for Fig 2.20(b). **(b)** Phasor diagram for Fig 2.20(c).

2.12 INDUCTOR/ CAPACITOR/ RESISTOR (LCR) A.C. CIRCUITS

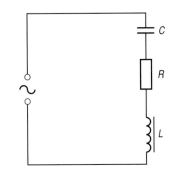

Fig 2.22 An *LCR* circuit.

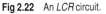

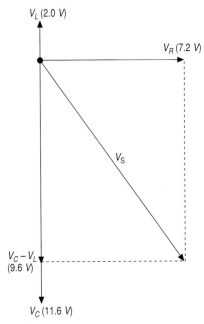

Fig 2.23 Phasor diagram.

2.13 RESONANCE

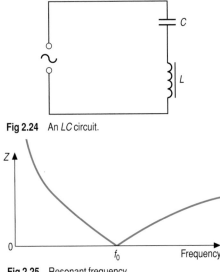

Fig 2.24 An *LC* circuit.

Fig 2.25 Resonant frequency.

In the *LCR* circuit in Fig 2.22, the a.c. is opposed by the capacitor, the inductor and the resistor. The total opposition to current in this case is called the **impedance** *Z*.

The *LCR* circuit in Fig 2.22 consists of an inductor of 80 mH, a capacitor of 22 µF and a resistor of 90 Ω. The circuit supply is 12 V, 50 Hz. For a frequency of 50 Hz, the reactance values are calculated to be

$$X_L = 25.1\,\Omega \qquad \text{and} \qquad X_C = 144.7\,\Omega$$

A voltmeter is used to measure the r.m.s. voltage across the components and the following results are obtained:

$$V_L = 2.0\,\text{V} \qquad V_C = 11.6\,\text{V} \qquad V_R = 7.2\,\text{V}$$

The r.m.s. voltage of the applied source is 12 V. According to Kirchhoff's second law, the vector sum of the r.m.s. voltages across each component must be equal to the supply p.d. The voltages across the components are not in phase since V_L leads V_R by 90°, V_C lags V_R by 90° and V_C lags V_L by 180°. The sum of the vectors can be determined from a **phasor** diagram (Fig 2.23).

The vector sum of the voltages, V_S, is the diagonal of the parallelogram, made up of $(V_C - V_L)$ and V_R and can be determined using Pythagoras' theorem (for values of $V_C > V_L$):

$$V_S^2 = V_R^2 + (V_C - V_L)^2$$
$$V_S = \sqrt{7.2^2 + (2.0 - 11.6)^2} \approx 12.0\,\text{V}$$
$$V_S = V_{\text{rms}}$$

An equation to calculate the impedance of the *LCR* circuit can be determined as follows:

$$V_L = IX_L \qquad V_C = IX_C \qquad V_R = IR$$

where *I* = r.m.s. current. Thus

$$V_S = \sqrt{I^2 R^2 + I^2 (X_C - X_L)^2} = I\sqrt{R^2 + (X_C - X_L)^2}$$

Therefore the impedance is

$$Z = \frac{V_S}{I} = \sqrt{R^2 + (X_C - X_L)^2}$$

The effect on the inductive reactance of increasing the frequency is the opposite to that on the capacitive reactance. This produces interesting results when a capacitor and an inductor are connected in series with an alternating voltage as in Fig 2.24.

At a certain frequency, known as the **series resonant frequency**, the capacitive reactance will be equal to the inductive reactance. The impedance of the series circuit is given by

$$Z = \sqrt{(X_L - X_C)^2}$$

At the resonant frequency $X_L = X_C$, and so the impedance of the circuit will be zero and the supply current will have a maximum value (infinite in the case of a perfect series resonant circuit supplied from an ideal voltage source). The circuit is said to be tuned to this resonant frequency (Fig 2.25).

At the resonant frequency, f_0

$$X_C = X_L \qquad \frac{1}{2\pi f_0 C} = 2\pi f_0 L \qquad f_0 = \frac{1}{2\pi\sqrt{LC}}$$

PASSIVE COMPONENTS

2.14 POWER IN *LCR* CIRCUITS

In the *LCR* circuit, no power is dissipated in the inductor or the capacitor (assuming they are ideal) in one complete a.c. cycle. Therefore the mean power $\overline{P}$ dissipated by the circuit is equal to the power dissipated in the resistor:

$$\overline{P} = I_{rms}^2 R$$

SUMMARY

Resistors can be identified from a colour code or printed code.

Inaccuracies occur in the manufacture of resistors and, for this reason, only certain preferred values are made.

Resistors in series: $R = R_1 + R_2 + R_3 + \ldots$

Resistors in parallel: $\dfrac{1}{R} = \dfrac{1}{R_1} + \dfrac{1}{R_2} + \dfrac{1}{R_3} + \ldots$

A capacitor can store charge and energy.

Capacitance, $C = \dfrac{\text{charge, } Q}{\text{potential difference, } V}$

Capacitors in series: $\dfrac{1}{C} = \dfrac{1}{C_1} + \dfrac{1}{C_2} + \dfrac{1}{C_3} + \ldots$

Capacitors in parallel: $C = C_1 + C_2 + C_3 + \ldots$

Time constant CR is the time it takes for a capacitor to discharge to 37% of its initial voltage or to charge to 63% of its final voltage.

The time for a capacitor to charge or discharge fully is $5CR$.

Capacitive reactance, $X_C = \dfrac{1}{2\pi f C}$

Inductive reactance, $X_L = 2\pi f L$

Resonant frequency, $f_0 = \dfrac{1}{2\pi\sqrt{LC}}$

Impedance of *LCR* circuit, $Z = \sqrt{R^2 + \left(X_C - X_L\right)^2}$

Chapter 3

SEMICONDUCTOR COMPONENTS

LEARNING OBJECTIVES

After studying this chapter you should be able to:

1. describe the characteristics of a diode;

2. describe the characteristics of bipolar and field-effect transistors;

3. know how to use transistors in switching circuits;

4. describe the action of other semiconductor components such as light-dependent resistors, thermistors, light-emitting diodes, photodiodes and phototransistors.

The **resistivity** of a material enables comparisons to be made between the conducting ability of different substances. The lower the resistivity of a material, the better conductor it is. Materials can be classified as **conductors**, **semiconductors** or **insulators** depending on their resistivities, as illustrated in Table 3.1. The enormous advances made in electronics over the last twenty years are due to the discovery and use of semiconducting materials. The ability of semiconductors to conduct electricity increases with increasing temperature, that is, the resistivity of a semiconductor falls as its temperature rises. Semiconductors are non-conductors at low temperatures. The most common semiconductor materials used in electronics are silicon (Si) and gallium arsenide (GaAs).

Table 3.1   Common materials used in electronics

Substance	Classification	Resistivity /Ω m at 25°C	Uses
Copper	Conductor	1.72×10^{-8}	Connecting wires
Gold	Conductor	2.42×10^{-8}	Microchip contacts
Carbon	Semiconductor	3.5×10^{-5}	Resistors
Silicon	Semiconductor	2300	Transistors
Gallium arsenide	Semiconductor	3.3×10^{6}	Light-emitting diodes
Polythene	Insulator	10^{14}	Wire insulation

3.1 THERMISTORS

The resistance of a conventional resistor is required to remain constant over a wide range of temperatures. **Thermistors** are designed so that their resistance changes markedly with temperature changes and are used for temperature-sensing applications. A thermistor is usually fabricated from a semiconducting material whose resistance changes with temperature. For a **negative temperature coefficient** (n.t.c.) thermistor an increase in temperature causes a decrease in its resistance. Rod, disc and bead types together with the circuit symbol for a thermistor are shown in Fig 3.1. The

(a)   (b)   (c)   (d)

small size of thermistors makes them ideal for measuring the temperature in small spaces.

Fig 3.1 Thermistor types: **(a)** rod, **(b)** disc and **(c)** bead; and **(d)** their symbol.

3.2 LIGHT-DEPENDENT RESISTORS

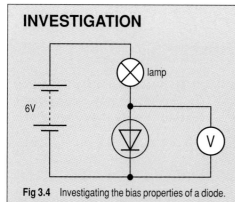

Fig 3.2 **(a)** The ORP12 light-dependent resistor and **(b)** its symbol.

A **light-dependent resistor** (LDR) consists of a disc of semiconducting material, usually cadmium sulphide. A typical LDR, the ORP12, is shown in Fig 3.2 together with the circuit symbol. When light falls on the LDR, its resistance decreases. Light-dependent resistors are used in many applications for measuring light levels, for example, in a camera to control the light exposure time.

3.3 DIODES

A typical silicon diode is shown in Fig 3.3 together with its circuit symbol.

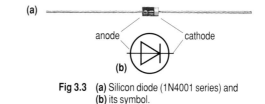

anode   cathode

Fig 3.3 **(a)** Silicon diode (1N4001 series) and **(b)** its symbol.

INVESTIGATION

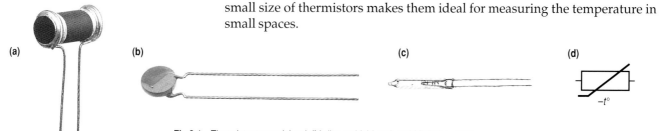

lamp

6V

V

Fig 3.4 Investigating the bias properties of a diode.

The bias properties of a diode

Basic apparatus: two clip component holders; 6 V, 60 mA MES lamp and holder; 1N4001 silicon diode; 6 V d.c. voltage supply; multimeter.

Construct the circuit as shown in Fig 3.4, and note the condition of the lamp. With the lamp illuminated, measure the p.d. across the diode. The meter should be set to a low d.c. voltage range, e.g. 2 V full-scale deflection (f.s.d.). Your answer should be in the region of 0.6 to 0.7 V. What happens when you reverse the diode?

When the diode allows current to pass, it is said to be **forward biased**. A voltage of about 0.7 V is developed across a silicon diode when it is forward biased, and this is called the **forward voltage**. The anode of the diode must be approximately 0.7 V more positive than the cathode before the diode can become forward biased and allow current to pass. When the diode was reversed in the previous investigation, the lamp did not light. When the cathode is more positive than the anode, the diode is said to be **reverse biased**, and only a very small reverse current is able to pass. This **one-way conduction property** of a diode is used to convert a.c. to d.c. in **rectifier** circuits.

Rectifiers

A rectifier makes use of the one-way conduction property of diodes to convert an a.c. signal from a transformer into d.c. **Half-wave rectification** is achieved using a single diode as shown in Fig 3.5. The problem with this arrangement is that half the power is cut off. **Full-wave rectification** is achieved using four diodes as in Fig 3.6, arranged so that both halves of the a.c. signal flow through the load resistor in the same direction. To achieve a more steady output, a large-value capacitor is connected across the load to 'smooth' the output. This circuit is called a **bridge rectifier** and is available as a single package IC.

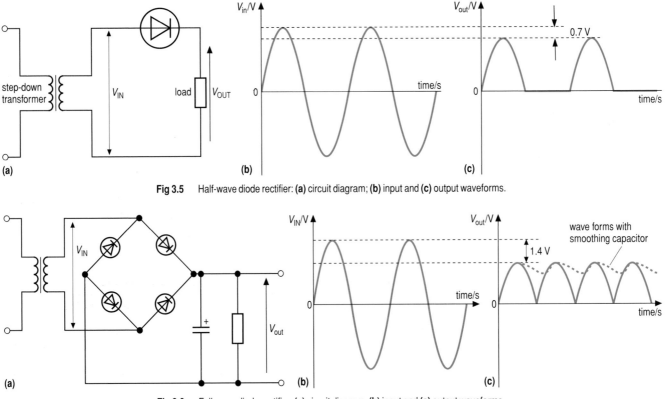

Fig 3.5   Half-wave diode rectifier: **(a)** circuit diagram; **(b)** input and **(c)** output waveforms.

Fig 3.6   Full-wave diode rectifier: **(a)** circuit diagram; **(b)** input and **(c)** output waveforms.

The disadvantage of these circuits is that, in both cases, there is a 0.7 V drop in voltage across the (silicon) diodes: 0.7 V is lost in the case of the single-diode half-wave rectifier and 1.4 V in the full-wave rectifier since the current flows through two diodes at any one time.

Diode characteristics

Fig 3.7 shows the characteristic curves for a typical silicon diode. Fig 3.7(a) shows how the forward current only rises once the forward voltage exceeds 0.7 V. Fig 3.7(b) shows that when the diode is reverse biased hardly any current passes unless the applied reverse bias voltage is large enough for the insulation properties of the diode to break down. The diode will then conduct when reverse biased and will not be able to recover its properties when this voltage is removed, i.e. it will suffer permanent damage.

The parameters of diodes to take note of are the **forward bias current** I_F, which is the maximum current that can pass through a diode when it is conducting, and the **peak inverse voltage PIV** (or the **maximum reverse repetitive voltage** V_{RRM}), which is the maximum reverse voltage allowed before the diode is damaged. A popular type of silicon diode is the 1N4000 series, which can conduct a maximum current of 1 A when forward biased. V_{RRM} ranges from 50 to 1000 V for this series.

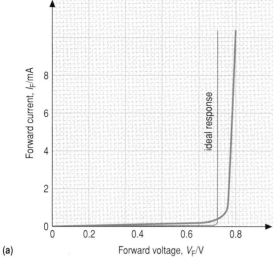

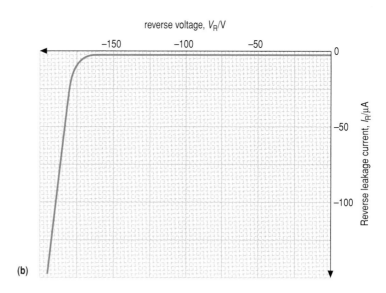

Fig 3.7 **(a)** Forward characteristic and **(b)** reverse characteristic for a typical silicon diode.

Diodes can be fabricated from another type of semiconducting material called **germanium**. Germanium diodes have a forward voltage of typically 0.2 V and they have lower forward currents than silicon diodes.

Diodes are often divided into **rectifier** or **signal** types. Rectifier diodes are designed to carry currents rated in amperes and are used in **rectifier** circuits in power supplies. Low-power signal diodes are used in radio circuits as they are able to respond to alternating p.d.'s changing at audio or radio frequencies. Table 3.2 summarises the characteristics of some common diodes.

Table 3.2   Characteristics of common semiconductor diodes

Diode	Material	I_F	PIV/V	Application
1N4148	Silicon	150 mA	75	General purpose
1N4001	Silicon	1 A	50	Low-voltage rectifier
OA91	Germanium	50 mA	115	Signal diode

3.4 ZENER DIODES

Zener marking
A Zener diode often has its Zener voltage marked on it such as 5V1, meaning that it can stabilise a 5.1 V supply.

True Zener diodes
'Zener' diodes are often referred to as breakdown diodes because many of these components do not rely on the Zener effect and have large breakdown voltages. True Zener diodes have a low value of reverse breakdown voltage.

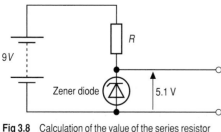

Fig 3.8   Calculation of the value of the series resistor for use with a Zener diode.

A **Zener diode** is specially made so that it breaks down in the reverse direction but is not permanently damaged provided the current through it is limited by a resistor. The characteristic curve is shown in Fig 3.9 on page 26. The Zener diode is designed to operate at its **peak inverse voltage** or **Zener reference voltage** V_Z because, in this region, current can flow through the diode but the voltage across it remains approximately stable. A Zener diode is used in power supply units to stabilise the output voltage even when varying currents are being drawn by the load connected to the power supply. Zener diodes are manufactured with a range of reference voltages in the E12 and E24 series (ranging from 2.4 to 91 V).

The action of a Zener diode is shown in Fig 3.8. A current-limiting series resistor is needed in order to prevent destruction of the Zener diode and the following calculation shows how to determine its value.

Example: Calculate the minimum value of the current-limiting series resistor in Fig 3.8 if the Zener diode (e.g. a BZYC5V1) has a power rating of 400 mW and has a reference voltage of 5.1 V.

Maximum reverse current is

$$I_{max} = \frac{power}{V_Z} = \frac{400 \times 10^{-3}}{5.1} = 0.078\,A$$

SEMICONDUCTOR COMPONENTS   **25**

P.d. across R is $V = 9 - 5.1 = 3.9\,\text{V}$

So

$$R = \frac{V}{I_{max}} = 49.7\,\Omega$$

0.078 A is the maximum current allowed through the diode so the nearest preferred value should be greater than 49.7 Ω, such as 56 Ω with a power rating (calculated from $P = I^2R$) of 1 W.

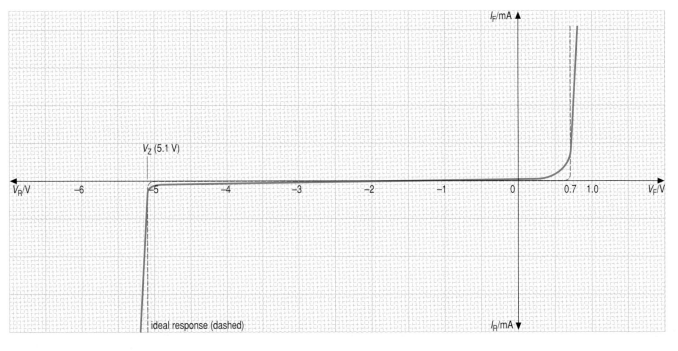

Fig 3.9 Current–voltage graph for a typical Zener diode.

3.5 REGULATORS

Zener diodes are inexpensive to buy and are suitable for stabilising the output voltage of low-power mains adapters. For more demanding applications, **integrated circuit regulators** are used. The 7805 is designed to produce a smooth, noise-free output of +5 V. A minimum input voltage of about 8 V is needed for the regulator to operate correctly due to a drop in potential across the circuit of typically 3 V. Fig 3.10 illustrates how external capacitors are connected to the regulator to produce a regulated supply voltage of +5 V. The 7805 is ideal for operating TTL logic integrated circuits which require a 5 V supply (see Chapter 5).

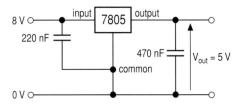

Fig 3.10 Using a regulator IC (7805) to produce a steady supply voltage of +5 V.

3.6 TRANSISTORS

Transistors fall into two main categories, **bipolar** and **field-effect**, and are also classified according to the semiconductor material from which they are fabricated, silicon or germanium. This chapter will consider both types of transistor and their use in switching circuits.

SEMICONDUCTOR COMPONENTS

3.7 BIPOLAR TRANSISTORS

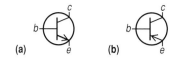

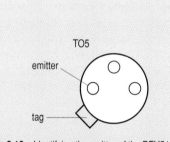

Fig 3.11 Symbols for **(a)** the npn transistor and **(b)** the pnp transistor.

There are two types of bipolar transistors, **npn** and **pnp**. Their circuit symbols are shown in Fig 3.11. Both types of transistor have three terminals, **base** *(b)*, **collector** *(c)* and **emitter** *(e)*. In its simplest form, the transistor can be made to act as a **solid-state** (no moving parts) switch which is either on or off. The following investigation demonstrates the switching action of a transistor.

INVESTIGATION

The switching action of a transistor

Basic apparatus: breadboard (see Appendix A for construction details); BFY51 transistor; 2.2 kΩ resistor; 10 kΩ potentiometer; 6 V, 60 mA MES lamp and holder; multimeter; regulated d.c. power supply with supply voltage, $V_{CC} = 6$ V.

Identifying the leads of the transistor: 'TO5' refers to the type of casing for the BFY51 transistor. Fig 3.12 shows the view underneath the case. The lead nearest the 'tag' is the emitter.

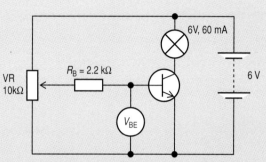

Fig 3.13 Investigating the switching action of an npn transistor.

Fig 3.12 Identifying the emitter of the BFY51 transistor.

Safety warning
Incorrect battery connection can seriously damage transistors.

Construct the circuit in Fig 3.13 on the breadboard. The breadboard construction is shown in Fig 3.14. Rotate the spindle of the potentiometer (VR) from one extreme to the other (from 0 to 10 kΩ) and note the condition of the lamp and the base voltage at which the lamp lights fully.

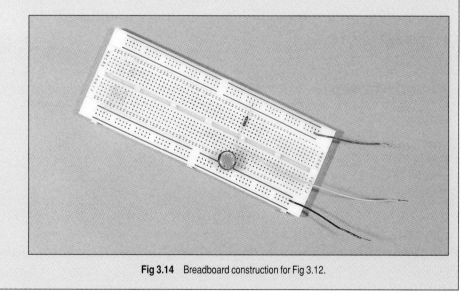

Fig 3.14 Breadboard construction for Fig 3.12.

The npn transistor

In the previous investigation, the lamp does not light until the voltage across the base and emitter terminals is approximately equal to 0.7 V. An npn transistor requires the base to be 0.7 V more positive than the emitter before the transistor will allow current to pass from the collector to the emitter, completing the circuit to the lamp, which then switches on. You might ask what the point of this is when there are mechanical switches which do the same job. However, transistors have an amplifying characteristic called **gain** which enables them to process signals provided by input systems. Gain is given the symbol h_{FE} and is determined by the formula:

$$h_{FE} = \frac{\text{collector current, } I_C}{\text{base current, } I_B}$$

The base current passes through the **base resistor, R_B,** and the collector current passes through the bulb into the collector terminal of the transistor. The base and collector currents combine in the transistor to become the emitter current, I_E, on passing out of the transistor.

The **emitter current I_E** is the sum of the collector and base currents:

$$I_E = I_B + I_C$$

The h_{FE} parameter for the BFY51 transistor is given in the supplier's data as 40 when the collector current is about 150 mA. This means that if the collector current is 150 mA then the base current is only 3.75 mA. Only a **small base current is required to switch on a larger collector current**. The simple transistor switch constructed in Fig 3.13 therefore acts as a **current amplifier**. In Fig 3.13, the collector current required for the lamp is 60 mA, so the base current needs to be 1.5 mA. R_B is included as a precaution so that when the potentiometer VR is moved round to +6 V, the base current is limited to a safe value to prevent damage to the transistor. At this point, the p.d. across R_B is $6 - 0.7 = 5.3$ V. The required base current is 1.5 mA so the value of the base resistor can be determined by:

$$R_B = \frac{5.3\text{ V}}{1.5\text{ mA}} = 3.5\text{ k}\Omega$$

The value for R_B used in Fig 3.13 was chosen to be lower than this calculated value to ensure that there is enough base current to switch the transistor on fully. The reason for the discrepancy is that the value given for h_{FE} is not very reliable and can vary enormously between different transistors, resulting in the transistor only being partly switched on and the lamp not being fully illuminated. This is explained in more detail in the next investigation.

The following investigation analyses in more detail the operating properties of the npn silicon transistor (BFY51).

INVESTIGATION

The operating properties of a transistor

Basic apparatus: breadboard; BFY51 transistor; 1 kΩ and 100 Ω resistors; 10 kΩ potentiometer; at least two multimeters; regulated d.c. power supply with supply voltage, $V_{CC} = 5$ to 12 V.

Construct the circuit in Fig 3.15 on the breadboard.

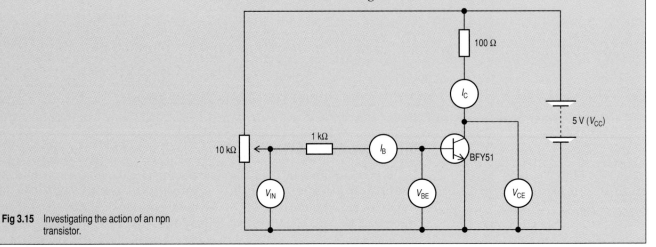

Fig 3.15 Investigating the action of an npn transistor.

SEMICONDUCTOR COMPONENTS

Draw up a results table as shown in Table 3.3. Use the potentiometer to vary the input voltage V_{IN} from 1.5 V to 0 V in steps of 0.1 V. Use a multimeter to measure the base emitter voltage V_{BE}, the base current I_B (use the 2 mA full-scale deflection (f.s.d.) setting), the collector current I_C (f.s.d. 200 mA) and the output voltage V_{CE} for each recorded value of V_{IN}. Plot graphs of: (a) I_C against V_{BE}, (b) I_C against V_{IN}, (c) I_C against I_B and (d) V_{CE} against V_{BE}.

Table 3.3   Results of the investigation

V_{IN}/V	V_{BE}/V	I_B/mA	I_C/mA	V_{CE}/V
1.5				
1.4				
etc.				
0.1				
0				

Analysis of the results obtained for the circuit in Fig 3.15

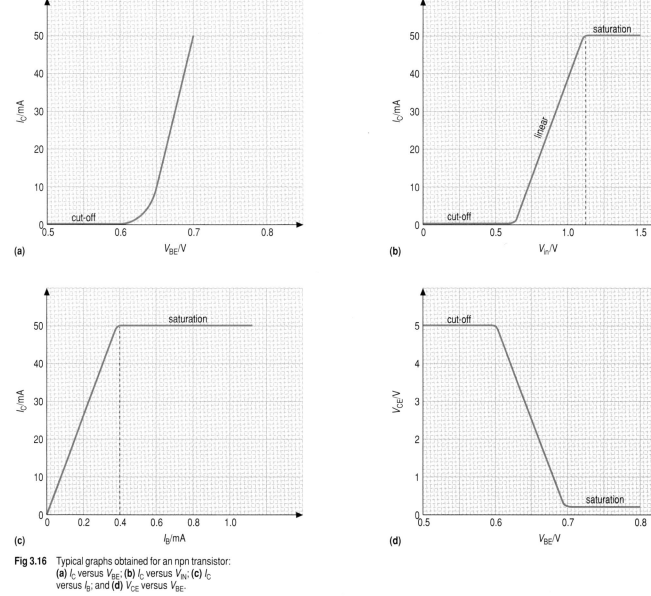

Fig 3.16 Typical graphs obtained for an npn transistor: (a) I_C versus V_{BE}; (b) I_C versus V_{IN}; (c) I_C versus I_B; and (d) V_{CE} versus V_{BE}.

The graphs obtained for the previous investigation should resemble the ones shown in Fig 3.16. Graphs (a) and (b) show that when V_{BE} and V_{IN} are below 0.6 V, the transistor is **cut off**, i.e. no collector current flows. When V_{BE} is between 0.6 and 0.7 V (and V_{IN} is between 0.6 and 1.1 V) the transistor switches on and the collector current increases until the transistor **saturates** (is fully switched on and cannot pass a larger current). During the sloping part of the graph the size of the collector current is controlled by the transistor and graph (c) shows that, in this linear region, the base current is approximately proportional to the collector current. In this region, the base current is amplified by a constant amount called the **large signal current gain, h_{FE}**, and is defined as:

$$h_{FE} = \frac{\text{steady collector current, } I_C}{\text{steady base current, } I_B}$$

This gain h_{FE} is measured for just one value of collector current, usually just when it reaches its saturation value.

In this example,

$$h_{FE} = \frac{I_C}{I_B} = \frac{50 \text{ mA}}{0.4 \text{ mA}} = 125$$

Typical values of h_{FE} for silicon transistors are given in Table 3.4.

Table 3.4   Characteristics of some common types of bipolar transistor

Code	Type	I_C(max) /mA	Power(max) /mW	h_{FE}(min–max)	Application
BC108	npn	100	300	110–800 @ 2 mA	General purpose, low power
BFY51	npn	1000	800	40(min) @ 150 mA	General purpose, low power
ZTX300	npn	500	300	50–300 @ 10 mA	General purpose, low power
2N3904	npn	200	350	100–300 @ 10 mA	Switching
BD131	npn	3000	15 000	20(min) @ 2 A	Power transistor
BC178	pnp	−100	300	125–500 @ −2 mA	General purpose, low power
ZTX500	pnp	−500	300	50–300 @ −10 mA	General purpose, low power

Classification
The European system for classifying transistors uses the first letter to indicate the type of semiconductor from which the transistor is made: A = germanium, e.g. A127; B = silicon, e.g. BFY51.

Si or Ge?
Silicon transistors are superior to germanium transistors for most applications, so germanium types are rarely encountered.

It is difficult to produce transistors with exact values for the gain because minute differences in the composition of the material can have significant effects on the gain. The range or minimum value for h_{FE} is given for a specific collector current. When selecting a transistor, the minimum gain must be able to provide the current gain required by the circuit.

The value of the base current at which saturation occurs is determined by the base resistance R_B. Using the data given in Fig 3.16(a) and (b), saturation occurs when $V_{IN} = 1.1$ V and $V_{BE} = 0.7$ V. Therefore the p.d. across R_B is $1.1 - 0.7 = 0.4$ V. Therefore, base current is

$$I_B = \frac{0.4 \text{ V}}{R_B} = \frac{0.4 \text{ V}}{1 \text{ k}\Omega} = 0.4 \text{ mA}$$

(as shown in Fig 3.16(c)).

When the transistor saturates, an increase in the base current does not lead to an increase in the collector current. The value of the collector current is determined by the output voltage and the load resistance R_L ('load' = a resistor through which the transistor drives a current). Fig 3.16(d) shows what happens to the output voltage as the transistor switches from cut-off to saturation. When V_{BE} is below 0.6 V the transistor is cut off and the output voltage V_{CE} equals the supply voltage V_{CC} (5.0 V) and there is no p.d. across R_L. As the transistor switches on, V_{CE} decreases until it is almost at 0 V when the transistor saturates. When $V_{CE} \approx 0\,\text{V}$ (this is about 0.2 V in practice), the p.d. across $R_L \approx 5\,\text{V}$.

When the transistor saturates,

$$I_C \approx \frac{\text{p.d. across } R_L}{R_L} = \frac{5\,\text{V}}{100\,\Omega} = 0.05\,\text{A (50 mA)}$$

(if V_{CE} is taken to be 0.2 V when the transistor saturates, $I_C = 48\,\text{mA}$). Then

collector emitter voltage = supply voltage to collector circuit
− p.d. across load resistor

i.e.

$$V_{CE} = V_{CC} - I_C R_L$$

In cut off,

$$V_{CE} = V_{CC} \qquad (I_C R_L = 0\,\text{V})$$

In saturation,

$$V_{CE} = 0\,\text{V} \quad \text{(ideally)} \qquad \text{and} \qquad V_{CC} = I_C R_L$$

QUESTIONS

Assume that, for saturation, $V_{BE} = 0.7\,\text{V}$ and $V_{CE} = 0.2\,\text{V}$.

3.1 A ZTX300 npn transistor operates with a collector current of 0.5 A and a base current of 10 mA. Determine the value of the emitter current and the d.c. gain.

3.2 The transistor in Fig 3.17 is just saturated. Use the data given in the diagram to calculate:
  (a) the base current,
  (b) the collector current and
  (c) the d.c. gain.

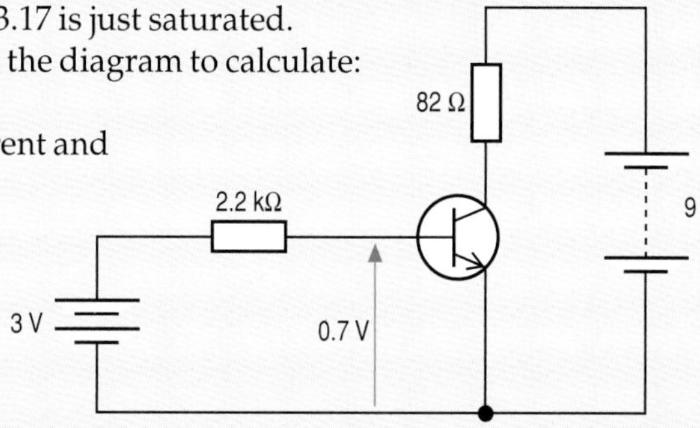

82 Ω

2.2 kΩ

9 V

3 V

0.7 V

Fig 3.17 Circuit for question 3.2.

The pnp transistor

The circuit constructed in Fig 3.13 used an npn transistor. The equivalent circuit can be constructed using a pnp transistor as shown in Fig 3.18. A pnp transistor requires the base to be 0.7 V more negative than the emitter before the transistor will allow current to pass from the emitter to the collector, completing the circuit to the lamp, which then switches on.

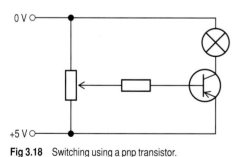

0 V

+5 V

Fig 3.18 Switching using a pnp transistor.

3.8 FIELD-EFFECT TRANSISTORS

The bipolar transistor is a current-controlled device whereas the field-effect transistor is a voltage-controlled device, i.e. its output current is controlled by the voltage across its input terminals.

There are two main types of FET, the **junction FET (JFET)** and the **metal oxide silicon FET (MOSFET)**.

The JFET

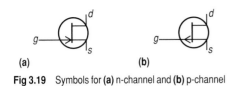

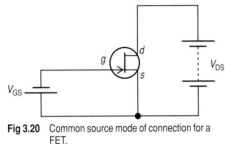

Fig 3.19 Symbols for **(a)** n-channel and **(b)** p-channel JFETs.

Both **n-channel** and **p-channel** JFETs are available. Their symbols are shown in Fig 3.19. The three terminals of a FET are called the **gate (g)**, **drain (d)** and **source (s)**. The main operational difference between the bipolar transistor and the FET is that the FET has a high input resistance and so the amount of current drawn by the gate is very small (of the order of nanoamperes, $1\,\text{nA} = 10^{-9}\,\text{A}$, for a JFET).

The n-channel JFET

The **common source mode** of connection is used mostly for FETs and this is shown in Fig 3.20.

Correct biasing is obtained by making the gate negative and the drain positive with respect to the source. V_{GS} is the voltage across the gate and source; V_{DS} is the voltage across the drain and source.

If V_{GS} is zero, the maximum number of electrons flow from the source to the drain so the **drain current I_{D}** is at its maximum. If V_{GS} is made increasingly negative, the drain current decreases until eventually it is zero.

Fig 3.20 Common source mode of connection for a FET.

JFET characteristics

The characteristic curve for a JFET can be obtained using the circuit in Fig 3.21.

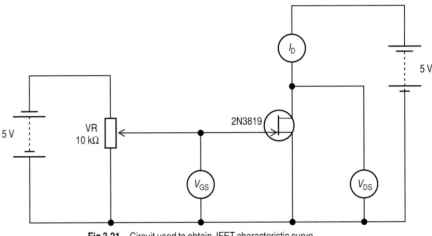

Fig 3.21 Circuit used to obtain JFET characteristic curve.

V_{DS} is set at 5 V and V_{GS} can be adjusted using the potentiometer VR. I_{D} is measured for various recorded values of V_{GS} as it is decreased from 0 V to –5 V. The transfer (or mutual, as it is sometimes called) characteristic curve is obtained by plotting I_{D} against V_{GS} (Fig 3.22). The maximum drain current flows when $V_{\text{GS}} = 0\,\text{V}$. As V_{GS} decreases (becomes more negative with respect to the source), the drain current falls. The relationship between V_{GS} and I_{D} is almost linear and provides information about the **mutual conductance** or **transconductance g** of the FET:

$$g = \frac{\Delta I_{\text{D}}}{\Delta V_{\text{GS}}}$$

where the symbol delta (Δ) means 'small change in'.

The unit of transconductance is the same as for conductance, and so is the siemens (S) (g corresponds to h_{FE} for a bipolar transistor).

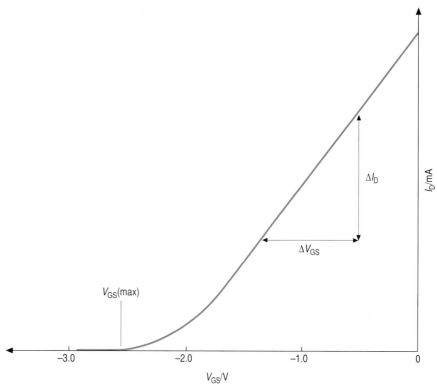

Fig 3.22   Characteristic curve showing the action of a JFET.

The use of a JFET as a switch

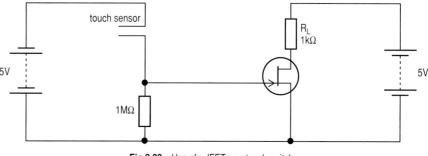

Fig 3.23   Use of a JFET as a touch switch.

V_{DD}
V_{DD} is the power supply voltage associated with the drain.

This is shown in Fig 3.23. When the sensor is touched (V_{GS} = max.), $I_D = 0$ and $V_{DS} = V_{DD} = 5$ V. When no contact is made with the sensor, $V_{GS} = 0$, I_D = max. and $V_{DS} = 0$ V.

When $V_{DS} = 0$ V, the p.d. across the load resistor is equal to the supply voltage, V_{DD}:

$$I_D = \frac{V_{DD}}{R_L} = \frac{5\,V}{1\,k\Omega} = 5\,mA$$

Historical note
The transistor (or transfer resistor as it was first called) was invented in 1948 by three Americans, Bardeen, Brattain and Shockley. They were awarded the 1956 Nobel Prize in Physics for their work.

The 2N3819 n-channel JFET is a low-power transistor (200 mW max.) so the maximum drain current would not be able to switch on a high-current device. If the load resistor is replaced with an LED and series resistor, the drain current will be sufficient to light the LED.

Note: The LED would light when no contact is made with the sensor and would go off when the sensor is touched.

Operation of p-channel JFET
To bias the p-channel JFET correctly, the drain must be negative and the gate positive with respect to the source.

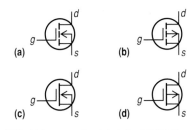

The MOSFET

The advantage of a MOSFET over a JFET is that the gate voltage can be positive or negative with respect to the source. The gate is completely insulated from the channel, connecting the drain to the source, by a thin layer of non-conducting silicon dioxide, giving the transistor a very high input resistance, without the need of reverse bias as is the case with the JFET.

There are two types of MOSFET, **enhancement** and **depletion**, both available in n- and p-channel forms. The symbols for the p-channel and n-channel enhancement and depletion MOSFETs are shown in Fig 3.24.

Action of the n-channel depletion type

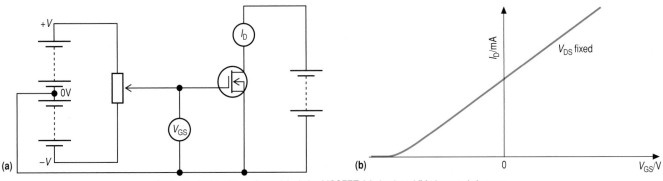

Fig 3.25 Action of an n-channel depletion MOSFET: **(a)** circuit and **(b)** characteristic curve.

This is shown in Fig 3.25. When $V_{GS} = 0$, I_D flows. If V_{GS} is made increasingly negative with respect to the source, I_D decreases until it is zero (as with the JFET). This is called the depletion mode. If V_{GS} is made positive with respect to the source, I_D increases. This is called the enhancement mode. A depletion-type MOSFET can operate in both modes.

Action of the n-channel enhancement type

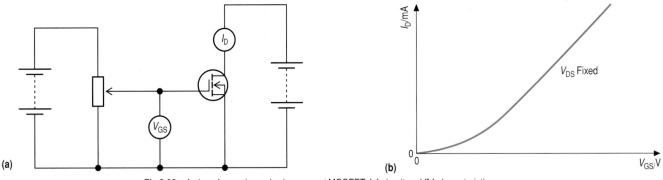

Fig 3.26 Action of an n-channel enhancement MOSFET: **(a)** circuit and **(b)** characteristic curve.

Transistor switch or relay?
Conventional electromagnetic relays will only operate at relatively slow speeds. In practice, many electronic circuits require fast switching speeds and these can only be achieved with solid-state devices such as a transistor switch. Other advantages of transistor switches are that they are inexpensive and small in size.

This is shown in Fig 3.26. When $V_{GS} = 0$, $I_D = 0$. If V_{GS} is made increasingly positive, I_D increases. This type can only operate in the enhancement mode.

Fig 3.27 shows how a MOSFET can be used as a touch switch. When no contact is made with the sensor, $V_{GS} = 0$, $I_D = 0$ and $V_{DS} = V_{DD} = 6.0$V. There is no p.d. across the lamp, so the lamp is off. When the sensor is touched, V_{GS} increases and I_D increases until $V_{DS} \approx 0$V (probably about 0.4V). The p.d. across the lamp is now 6V and the lamp lights.

QUESTION	
	3.3 An n-channel FET operates with a drain current of 25 mA and a gate–source bias of −1 V. If the transconductance of the FET is 3mS, calculate the new drain current if the bias voltage increases to −2 V.

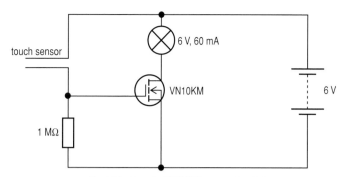

Fig 3.27   Use of a MOSFET as a touch switch.

Applications of transistors

Early commercial applications for transistors included very small hearing aids and compact portable radios. Transistors were also used in miniaturised diagnostic instruments used to transmit data from the bodies of astronauts on space flights. Miniature radio transmitters using transistors have been implanted in animals to study ecological factors. During the late 1960s, a new electronic technique, the integrated circuit (IC), began to replace the transistor in complex electronic equipment.

3.9 INTEGRATED CIRCUITS

An **integrated circuit** (IC) is a miniature electronic circuit (Fig 3.28) made using a technique called **photolithography**. An IC contains microscopically small components such as transistors, diodes, capacitors and resistors connected together on a 'chip' of wafer-thin silicon no more than 5 mm square. The IC is packaged in a plastic case to protect it, with connection made from the chip to the metal pins of the **package**. An IC can be **dedicated** to perform a specific function, such as to 'flash' an LED (LM3909) or to convert an analogue voltage into a digital output (ZN427E), or it may be able to perform many different functions when assembled with external components (different uses of the 555 timer IC and the 081 operational amplifier IC will be considered in later chapters). Fig 3.29(a) shows a wafer of silicon containing hundreds of identical integrated circuits and Fig 3.29(b) shows part of an IC in its protective 'dual in-line' package with part of the package cut away to reveal the IC. The 1970s saw the production of medium-, large- and very-large-scale integrated circuits (MSI, LSI and VLSI), which have enabled compact computers to be produced.

Fig 3.28   An example of microminiaturisation. This integrated circuit (a F-100 microprocessor) is only 0.6 mm square and is small enough to pass through the eye of a needle.

Fig 3.29   (a) A silicon chip wafer. (b) Part of an integrated circuit (IC) is seen here within a computer microchip. An IC consists of many circuit elements such as transistors and resistors fabricated on a single piece of silicon or other semiconducting material. The tiny microprocessor shown is the heart of the personal computer (PC). Such devices may contain several million transistors and be able to execute over 100 million instructions per second. The rows of leg-like metal pins are used to connect the microprocessor to a circuit board.

(a)

(b)

3.10 PHOTODIODES

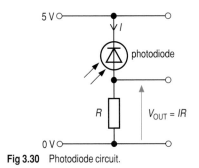

Fig 3.30 Photodiode circuit.

An ordinary diode is sensitive to light, but light is usually excluded by sealing the diode in a plastic light-proof package. A **photodiode** has a transparent case or window which allows light to fall onto the diode.

The photodiode is connected in reverse bias (Fig 3.30) and when light falls on the 'window' the reverse current is greatly increased and increases proportionally to the incident light intensity.

The photocurrent for a typical photodiode varies from about 1 nA in the dark to 100 μA in bright light. The arrangement in Fig 3.30 can be used to produce a voltage change which corresponds to the change in light intensity, but the resistor value R must be large (typically 1 MΩ) to produce a measurable output voltage. The casing of infrared photodiodes is transparent to infrared but opaque to visible light. Infrared photodiodes are used in security systems and in TV and video remote-control systems.

3.11 PHOTO-TRANSISTORS

Typical **phototransistors** are constructed in either a transparent plastic case or a metal case with a glass window in the top. The base is usually left disconnected. When light falls on the transistor, a small current passes from the base to the emitter, switching on a larger collector emitter current. Phototransistors are more sensitive than photodiodes but have relatively slower response times. Integrated circuits are now available which contain both a photodiode and an amplifier in the same IC, therefore combining sensitivity with a response. The development of these ICs means that phototransistors are rarely used.

3.12 LIGHT-EMITTING DIODES

Fig 3.31 A light-emitting diode (LED).

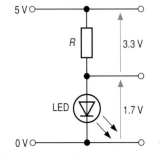

Fig 3.32 Calculation of the value of the series resistor for use with an LED.

The development of the light-emitting diode (LED) (Fig 3.31) in the 1970s stemmed from research into light sources for use with optical fibres. A common use for LEDs is now as a replacement for filament lamps in panel indicators, particularly for 'stand-by' indicators, due to the low power consumption of LEDs. When LEDs were first manufactured, only red was available. It is now possible to produce a range of colours by varying the composition of the semiconductor from which the LED is made. Standard LEDs are made from the semiconductor gallium arsenide phosphide. When the LED is forward biased it conducts and emits red, green, yellow or orange light. The use of silicon carbide as the semiconductor material has made possible the manufacture of blue LEDs. An LED will not conduct if it is reverse biased and care should be taken to connect the LED the correct way round with its cathode towards 0 V because if the reverse voltage exceeds 5 V the LED may be damaged. The data shown in Table 3.5 for standard LEDs show that the typical forward voltage for the red LED to emit light is 1.7 V, with a maximum forward current of 20 mA. A series resistor (Fig 3.32) is needed to protect the LED. Shown below is the way to calculate the value of the resistor using $R = V/I$ and the LED data.

The p.d. across R is $5 - 1.7 = 3.3$ V. So

$$R = \frac{3.3\,\text{V}}{20\,\text{mA}} = 0.165\,\text{k}\Omega$$

Table 3.5   LED data

	I_F(max)/mA	V_F(typ)/V	V_F(max)/V	V_R(max)/V
Red	20	1.7	2	5
HE red	20	2	2.5	5
Bright red	20	2	2.8	5
Green	20	2.2	2.5	5
Yellow	20	2.1	2.5	5
Amber	20	2	2.5	5

Source: RS Catalogue.

SEMICONDUCTOR COMPONENTS

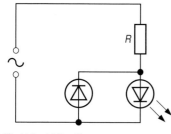

Fig 3.33 Using LEDs with a.c.

Red LED = on
Red is the universal colour for indicating that a circuit is energised.

20 mA is the maximum forward current the LED can pass, so in order to limit the current to a safe value, the nearest preferred value should be chosen which is greater than the calculated value, i.e. 180 Ω.

When using an LED with alternating current, it must be protected from the reverse voltages which exceed the reverse voltage rating of the LED. This is achieved by connecting a diode in parallel with the LED as in Fig 3.33. The protection diode conducts on the half-cycles when the LED would otherwise be reverse biased. An approximate value for the series resistor R can be calculated from the equation:

$$R = \frac{V_{\text{rms}} - V_{\text{F}}}{2I_{\text{F}}}$$

where V_{rms} is the r.m.s. supply voltage, V_{F} is the d.c. value of the forward voltage and I_{F} is the d.c. value of the forward current.

QUESTIONS

3.4 A low-current LED has a forward voltage of 2.0 V and is operated from a 6 V d.c. supply. Determine the value of the series resistor required if the LED is to pass a current of 2 mA.

3.5 Calculate the series resistor required to operate the LED in question 3.4 from a 6 V r.m.s. a.c. supply if its mean forward current is rated at 2 mA.

A glance through the 'Optoelectronics' section of a components catalogue will illustrate the numerous types of LED available. Look for bi-colour (and tri-colour) types which emit red or green light depending on which way round they are connected, and are useful for polarity indication. Flashing LEDs are also available which incorporate a miniature circuit to make the LED flash continually.

3.13 OPTO-ISOLATORS

Opto-isolators or opto-couplers use an infrared-emitting diode and a photo-diode or phototransistor. An opto-isolator enables a circuit to be electrically isolated from associated circuits. This is useful for computer input interfacing since computers can be easily damaged if too high a supply voltage (usually above 5 V) is connected to their input. The circuit in Fig 3.34 shows how a typical opto-isolator (4N38X) can be used as a computer input interface.

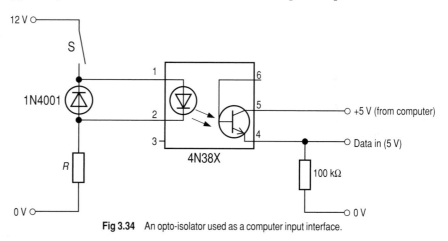

Fig 3.34 An opto-isolator used as a computer input interface.

When switch S is closed, a beam of infrared light is directed at the phototransistor, switching it on and allowing current from the 5 V computer supply making the voltage at 'Data in' nearly 5 V. 'Data in' can be switched

---

SEMICONDUCTOR COMPONENTS

from 'high' (5 V) to 'low' (0 V) without connection between any external voltage and the computer.

(The 1N4001 diode is used to protect the infrared-emitting diode from too high a reverse voltage. If the input connections are the wrong way round, current would then flow through the protection diode rather than through the infrared-emitting diode.)

SUMMARY

Semiconductors are used in a wide variety of devices, including diodes, transistors and integrated circuits.

A silicon diode only conducts when it has a forward voltage of 0.7 V.

A Zener diode operates at its peak inverse voltage to give a constant voltage for a wide range of currents.

Transistors can be npn or pnp bipolar or field-effect types.

For a bipolar transistor, $I_E = I_B + I_C$ and $h_{FE} = \dfrac{I_C}{I_B}$

A bipolar transistor is operated as a switch at cut-off and at saturation.

For a FET, transconductance, $g = \dfrac{\Delta I_D}{\Delta V_{GS}}$

Light-emitting diodes emit light when forward biased. A typical forward voltage for a standard LED is 2 V.

Chapter 4

INPUT AND OUTPUT CIRCUITS

LEARNING OBJECTIVES

After studying this chapter you should be able to:

1. understand the principles of and the use of input sensors in potential divider circuits;

2. appreciate that the transistor can be used as a switch to interface a potential divider circuit and output device;

3. understand the principle of and the use of input sensors in bridge circuits;

4. state what an output transducer does and give examples;

4.1 INPUT DEVICES

The word **transducer** is often used to describe these devices. This can be misleading since a transducer is defined as a component which converts energy into different forms. The resistance of a light-dependent resistor (LDR) depends on the amount of light falling on the component, and this resistance change is converted to a voltage change by means of a potential divider circuit. Light-dependent resistors, thermistors and strain gauges are sometimes referred to as resistive transducers, as their resistance changes under various external conditions but, strictly speaking, they are not transducers because they do not convert energy into other forms.

Some input sensors *are* transducers (often referred to as **active** transducers). A thermocouple converts thermal energy into electrical energy and some types of microphone, for example, moving coil and crystal types, convert sound energy into electrical energy.

The purpose of an input device is to change the surrounding physical variations of light, temperature and moisture, for example, into electrical variations that can be processed by the electronic system.

4.2 LIGHT-DEPENDENT RESISTOR

Light-dependent resistors can be used for smoke detection, automatic lighting control, batch counting and alarm systems. Fig 4.1 illustrates a system constructed from Alpha kit modules which could be used for counting the number of items that interrupt a light beam directed at the LDR. The display increases by one when the LDR is made alternately dark then light.

Fig 4.1 Alpha kit system, showing a light-sensing unit connected to a counter/driver display module.

Data for the ORP12

When light falls on the LDR, its resistance decreases. The actual variation of resistance (in kΩ) with illumination (in lux) is given in a data sheet (RS F14188) and is reproduced here as Fig 4.2. Data are also provided on the illumination of various light sources, as shown in Table 4.1.

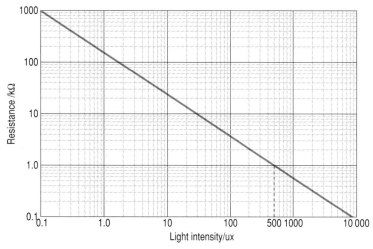

Table 4.1   Data for ORP12: guide to source illuminations

Light source	Illumination (lux)
Moonlight	0.1
60 W bulb at 1 m	50
1 W MES bulb at 0.1 m	100
Fluorescent lighting	500
Bright sunlight	30 000

Source: RS Data Sheet F14188, March 1994.

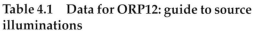

Fig 4.2   A log–log graph showing the variation of resistance with light intensity for an LDR.

The relationship between resistance and illumination is not linear since the graph scale is logarithmic.

QUESTION

4.1 Determine from the graph in Fig 4.2 the resistance of the LDR when it is illuminated **(a)** in fluorescent lighting and **(b)** by a 60 W bulb placed 1 m from the LDR.

INPUT AND OUTPUT CIRCUITS

4.3 POTENTIAL DIVIDERS

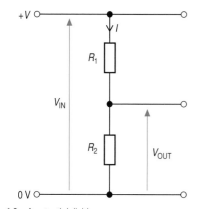
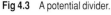
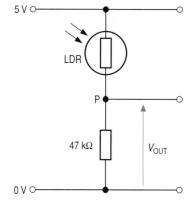

Fig 4.3 A potential divider.

Fig 4.4 A light-sensing potential divider.

The change in resistance of an LDR with light intensity can be converted to a voltage change using a **potential divider** circuit. We shall derive a **formula for potential divider circuits.** The symbols used refer to Fig 4.3. The current through the resistors is

$$I = \frac{\text{p.d. across resistors, } V_{IN}}{\text{total resistance, } R_1 + R_2}$$

The p.d. across resistor R_2 is

$$V_{OUT} = IR_2$$

Therefore

$$V_{OUT} = \frac{R_2}{R_1 + R_2} V_{IN}$$

Example: Consider the light-sensing potential divider circuit in Fig. 4.4: Calculate V_{OUT} when the LDR is illuminated by **(a)** moonlight and **(b)** fluorescent lighting.

(a) In moonlight, the resistance of the LDR is about $1000\,k\Omega$ (obtained from the graph in Fig 4.2). We use

$$V_{OUT} = \frac{R_2}{R_1 + R_2} V_{IN}$$

where V_{IN} is the supply voltage, R_1 is the resistance of the LDR and R_2 is the value of the fixed resistor. Thus

$$V_{OUT} = \frac{47\,k\Omega}{(1000 + 47)\,k\Omega} \times 5\,V = 0.22\,V$$

The potential at point P is $0.22\,V$ in moonlight.

(b) In fluorescent lighting, the resistance of the LDR is about $1\,k\Omega$ (Fig 4.2). So

$$V_{OUT} = \frac{47\,k\Omega}{(1 + 47)\,k\Omega} \times 5\,V = 4.90\,V$$

The potential at point P is $4.90\,V$ in fluorescent lighting.

For the same light intensity conditions the output voltage can be reversed so that a high voltage is obtained when the LDR is dark. This can be done by simply interchanging the LDR and resistor and is demonstrated in question 4.2.

QUESTION

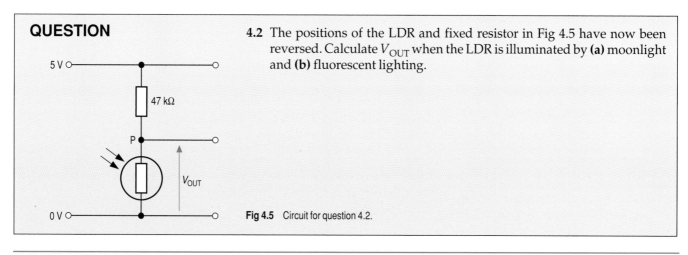

4.2 The positions of the LDR and fixed resistor in Fig 4.5 have now been reversed. Calculate V_{OUT} when the LDR is illuminated by **(a)** moonlight and **(b)** fluorescent lighting.

Fig 4.5 Circuit for question 4.2.

Light-dependent resistors are inexpensive and more simple to use than other light sensors (such as photodiodes and phototransistors) but they have slow response times. The time it takes for the resistance of an LDR to respond to a change in illumination is of the order of milliseconds, taking longer to respond to an increase than to a decrease in illumination.

Photodiodes are more expensive than light-dependent resistors, especially large-area types, but they operate over a wider spectral range and can respond much faster than the LDR. This property enables them to be used in high-speed pulse detection circuits, alarm and remote control systems.

4.4 REFLECTIVE OPTO-SWITCH

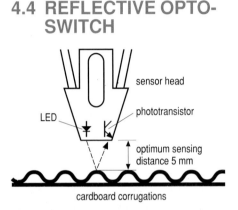

Fig 4.6   Use of a reflective opto-switch.

Another type of light-sensing device is a **reflective opto-switch,** which contains an infrared-emitting diode and a phototransistor housed in a plastic package. The phototransistor responds to radiation from the diode when a reflective object is placed in the field of view. These devices have many applications. One industrial use involves measuring the required length of corrugated cardboard needed to provide the packaging for fluorescent lamp tubes. The reflective opto-switch and associated control circuit are set up to sense and count the regular corrugations (undulations) on the cardboard. After a set number of corrugations have been detected, for the required length, the cardboard is cut. Fig 4.6 shows how, when a wave crest passes, the infrared beam is reflected onto the phototransistor but, when a trough passes, the phototransistor is outside the path of the reflected infrared beam.

4.5 THERMISTOR

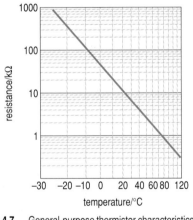

Fig 4.7   General-purpose thermistor characteristics.

The resistance of a thermistor changes with temperature. If a thermistor has a **negative temperature coefficient** (n.t.c.) its resistance decreases with increase in temperature. If the thermistor has a **positive temperature coefficient** (p.t.c.) its resistance increases with increase in temperature.

Data sheets on thermistors often include formulae and graphs for determining the resistance of a thermistor at a particular temperature. A general-purpose n.t.c. thermistor has the characteristic graph shown in Fig 4.7. Note that the scale is **logarithmic**.

QUESTION	4.3 The relationship between resistance and temperature for a particular thermistor is shown in Fig 4.7. The resistance of the thermistor at $25\,°C$ is $10\,k\Omega$. What is the resistance of the thermistor at $100\,°C$? At what temperature is the resistance $30\,k\Omega$?

This change in resistance can be converted to a voltage change using a potential divider circuit as shown in Fig 4.8.

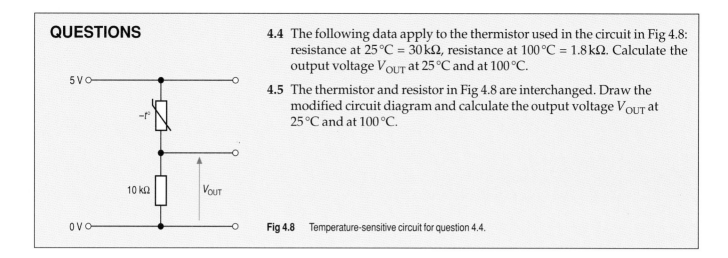

4.4 The following data apply to the thermistor used in the circuit in Fig 4.8: resistance at 25 °C = 30 kΩ, resistance at 100 °C = 1.8 kΩ. Calculate the output voltage V_{OUT} at 25 °C and at 100 °C.

4.5 The thermistor and resistor in Fig 4.8 are interchanged. Draw the modified circuit diagram and calculate the output voltage V_{OUT} at 25 °C and at 100 °C.

Fig 4.8 Temperature-sensitive circuit for question 4.4.

4.6 TRANSISTOR SWITCH

A transistor switch can be used as the process block together with the potential divider circuits described so far to construct simple light-sensitive and temperature-sensitive switches. A light-sensitive switch circuit is shown in Fig 4.9. When the LDR is dark, most of the 6 V supply voltage is dropped across the LDR due to its high resistance. The transistor saturates, switching on the collector current, which is large enough to light the lamp. When light falls on the LDR, its resistance decreases and the input voltage falls. If the resistance falls low enough, the transistor will be cut off and the lamp will not light. If the LDR and the variable resistor are interchanged, the lamp will be lit when the LDR is illuminated and will not be lit when the LDR is darkened. The desired switching voltages can be adjusted using the variable resistor.

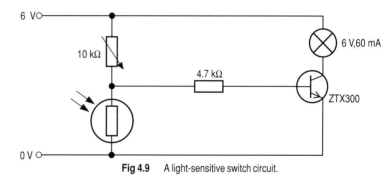

Fig 4.9 A light-sensitive switch circuit.

4.7 WHEATSTONE BRIDGE CIRCUIT

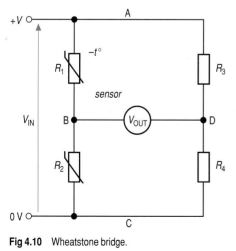

Fig 4.10 Wheatstone bridge.

When a thermistor is used in a potential divider circuit, there is a current through it. This current will heat the thermistor, causing its resistance to change (**self-heating**). This can be avoided by using a '**dummy**' thermistor in a Wheatstone bridge circuit. Fig 4.10 shows the Wheatstone bridge arrangement, which consists of two potential dividers with one of them used as a reference. The sensor, the thermistor, is placed in arm AB and an identical dummy thermistor, which is not subject to the temperature change, in arm BC. The bridge is said to be **balanced** when $V_{OUT} = 0$, i.e. when the potential at B is equal to the potential at D. Balance occurs when

$$\frac{R_1}{R_2} = \frac{R_3}{R_4}$$

When the temperature of the sensor thermistor changes, resistance R_1 changes, which upsets the balance and produces a measurable change in V_{OUT}. The purpose of the dummy thermistor is to overcome the self-heating problem. Any change in the resistance of R_1 due to the current will produce an identical change in the resistance R_2, so the ratio R_1/R_2 is unchanged.

Thermistors can be used for temperature control in ovens and freezers.

4.8 STRAIN GAUGE

Fig 4.11 Undercarriage strain gauges monitor forces in testing.

Strain gauges are used extensively in engineering to measure the strains in structures. For example, undercarriages of aeroplanes (Fig 4.11) are subjected to enormous compressive and tensile stresses when they land. Rigorous testing is carried out at the manufacturing plants, using strain gauges to monitor the strains in the undercarriage when it is acted on by various forces. Fig 4.12 shows a typical **strain gauge** which is used to measure strains in a structure.

If the structure is subjected to tensile strains, the foil stretches, increasing in length and resistance. The small change in resistance of the strain gauge can be converted to a voltage change using a Wheatstone bridge circuit and an amplifier as in Fig 4.13.

Fig 4.12 A strain gauge.

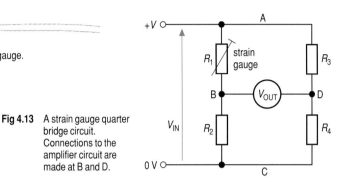

Fig 4.13 A strain gauge quarter bridge circuit. Connections to the amplifier circuit are made at B and D.

When there is no strain, the resistors are arranged so that the bridge is balanced and V_{OUT} is zero. At balance point, $R_1/R_2 = R_3/R_4$. If the strain increases and the gauge is stretched, R_1 increases, causing the bridge to be unbalanced, resulting in a measurable change in the output voltage.

Example: Consider the following strain gauge data: gauge length $L = 8\,\text{mm}$, measurable strain = 3 to 4% of length, gauge factor $K = 2.1$, gauge resistance $R_1 = 120\,\Omega$. The gauge factor is given by the formula

$$K = \frac{\Delta R}{R}\frac{L}{\Delta L}$$

where ΔR is the change in resistance of the gauge and ΔL is the extension/compression.

Calculate the output voltage of the so-called **quarter bridge** in Fig 4.13 when the strain gauge is stretched by 1% extension of its original length; $R_2 = 120\,\Omega$, $R_3 = 1\,\text{k}\Omega$, $R_4 = 1\,\text{k}\Omega$; $V = 5\,\text{V}$.

The extension ΔL is 1% of the original gauge length ($L = 8\,\text{mm}$), i.e.

$$\Delta L = 0.01 \times 8\,\text{mm} = 0.08\,\text{mm}$$

Now we can use the above formula, rewritten as

$$\Delta R = \frac{KR_1\Delta L}{L}$$

So

$$\Delta R = \frac{2.1 \times 120 \times 0.08}{8} = 2.52\,\Omega$$

and the new gauge resistance R_1 is $120 + 2.52 \approx 122.5\,\Omega$. Now we can use $I = V_B/R_2 = V_{IN}/(R_1 + R_2)$ to obtain

$$\text{potential at } B = \frac{120}{122.5 + 120} \times 5 = 2.47\,\text{V}$$

Similarly potential at $D = 2.50\,\text{V}$. Therefore

$$V_{OUT} = 2.50 - 2.47 = 0.03\,\text{V}$$

A more sensitive method for measuring the resistance change is to use a **full bridge** as illustrated in Fig 4.14. The sensors are arranged so that R_2 and R_3 are being compressed and R_1 and R_4 are being stretched. This arrangement will produce the greatest possible p.d. across BD. If the strain on a cantilever beam is to be measured, the gauges could be arranged as in Fig 4.15.

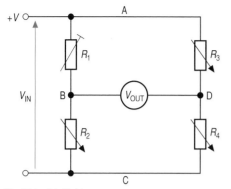

Fig 4.14   A full bridge.

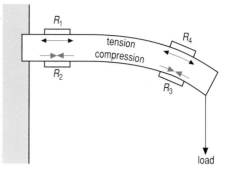

Fig 4.15   Arrangement of strain gauges on a cantilever.

QUESTION

4.6 If the strain gauges used in Fig 4.14 are of the same type as used in the previous example, calculate the output voltage when the extension/compression of each strain gauge causes a change in resistance of $2.52\,\Omega$.

4.9 MECHANICAL SWITCHES*

Historical note:
The first telephone switching systems were manually operated. The operator would connect calls by physically plugging wires into a board. The operator had to monitor the connections and so privacy was not always maintained. It was the unscrupulous behaviour of one switchboard operator that led to the development of the first automatic switching system.

Almon Strowger was an undertaker in Kansas City, USA. He was concerned that his telephone never seemed to ring and suspected that it might have something to do with the operator. After some enquiries he discovered that she was the wife of his main business rival, and every time a request was made to connect to Strowger she redirected the call to her own husband to increase his business. In 1889 Strowger patented a switch which worked automatically from pulses of current produced as the caller dialled the number. The connection was therefore made without the need of an operator.

There are a large number of different types of switch available, each having its own special use. Switches are defined in terms of **poles** and **throws**. Pole refers to the number of different circuits that can be controlled and throw (or way) describes the number of alternative connections available. Examples of mechanical switches include toggle or rocker types, slide switches, push-to-make and push-to-break which can be momentary or latching (i.e. push to switch 'on' and push again to switch 'off'), rotary switches, micro-switches and tilt switches.

4.10 MAGNETIC SWITCHES

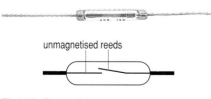

unmagnetised reeds

Fig 4.16   Reed switch.

Reed switch

A **reed** switch (Fig 4.16) consists of two springy reeds made from a ferromagnetic material (one which can be easily magnetised and demagnetised), sealed in a glass tube which contains an inert gas to prevent the springy contacts corroding. A coil is wrapped around the reed switch and, when current flows through the coil, the induced magnetism makes the reed switch close. When the current is turned off, the reed switch opens.

* This section is taken from 'Historical background of switches', *Electronics Education*, Summer 1994.

Reed **proximity** switches are designed to close (or open) when a magnet is brought near to the reed switch. These are often used as the sensors in intruder circuits as in Fig 4.17. The reed switch is attached to the door frame and the magnet to the door. When the door is opened (by an intruder) the magnet is pulled away from the reed switch, thereby activating the alarm circuit.

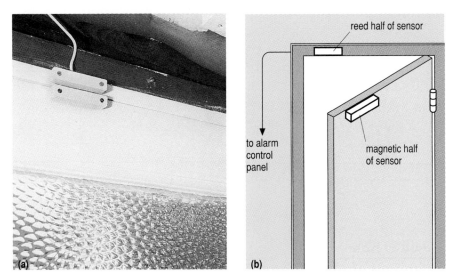

Fig 4.17 Use of a reed switch, in an alarm circuit, as a door sensor.

Hall effect switch

When a semiconductor is placed in a magnetic field, a p.d. is developed across it. This is known as the Hall effect. Hall effect IC switches are available which can be connected as shown in Fig 4.18 to act as a magnetically operated switch. When a magnetic south pole is within 2 mm of the sensitive face of the IC, $V_{OUT} \approx 0\,V$, and when the magnet is removed, $V_{OUT} \approx 5\,V$. Hall effect switches are used in tachometers to measure the rate of rotation of a machine. The advantage of this type of switch is that it does not exhibit 'bounce' (see Chapter 7).

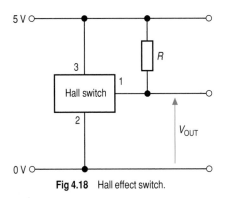

Fig 4.18 Hall effect switch.

4.11 OUTPUT DEVICES

Light-emitting diodes, lamps, loudspeakers, buzzers, motors and relay switches are all examples of **output transducers** which convert electrical energy into another form of energy. The **relay**, which converts electrical energy into mechanical energy, will be considered in the next section.

4.12 RELAY

Microelectronic circuits are required to control many devices which need a much greater current than the control circuit can supply. In these cases, relays are sometimes used. Relays are electromagnetic switches which can use small currents to switch on or off large currents, the coil only consuming a fraction of the power the contacts can switch.

Relay specifications

- *Coil voltage:* the voltage at which the relay is designed to operate.
- *Coil resistance:* this can be used to calculate the current flowing through the coil.
- *Switch contact rating:* the maximum voltage that the relay can 'switch on'.
- *Contact arrangement:* various contact arrangements (Fig 4.19) are available which include SPCO (single pole changeover) or SPDT (single pole double throw), and DPCO (double pole changeover) or DPDT (double pole double throw). The symbols used refer to those often sketched in component catalogues.

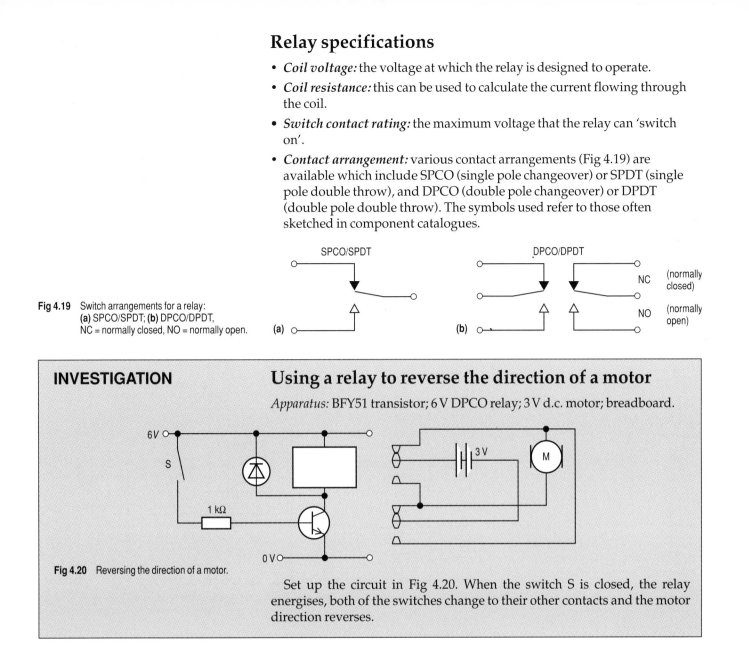

Fig 4.19 Switch arrangements for a relay:
(a) SPCO/SPDT; (b) DPCO/DPDT,
NC = normally closed, NO = normally open.

INVESTIGATION Using a relay to reverse the direction of a motor

Apparatus: BFY51 transistor; 6 V DPCO relay; 3 V d.c. motor; breadboard.

Fig 4.20 Reversing the direction of a motor.

Set up the circuit in Fig 4.20. When the switch S is closed, the relay energises, both of the switches change to their other contacts and the motor direction reverses.

Use of a protection diode

When a relay or other electromagnetic device switches off, there is a surge in potential across the coil (the back e.m.f.), as a result of electromagnetic induction, which can damage any electronic circuit used to control the current through the relay coil. In Fig 4.20 a diode is connected across the coil to protect the transistor from this back e.m.f. The diode can be any silicon type, for example, the 1N4001 to 1N4006 series.

QUESTION

4.7 Describe the action of the circuit in Fig 4.21.

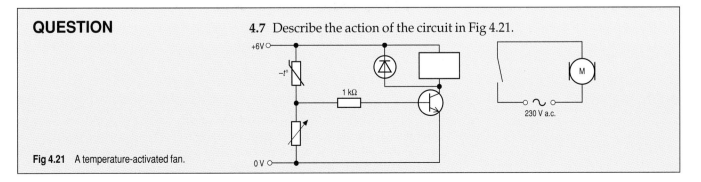

Fig 4.21 A temperature-activated fan.

Transistorised motor control*

The use of a relay to reverse a motor in Fig 4.20 is not the best method since switching the relay whilst the motor is in motion will cause unnecessary wear. A better solution is to use transistor switches. The circuit diagram is shown in Fig 4.22. TR_1, TR_2, TR_3 and TR_5 are npn transistors which conduct when their base terminal is 0.7 V more positive than their emitter terminal. TR_4 and TR_6 are pnp transistors which conduct when their base voltage is 0.7 V below their emitter voltage. When input 1 is connected to 3 V and input 2 connected to 0 V, TR_1 is switched on, causing the voltage at point A to fall to 0 V. Therefore the bases of TR_3 and TR_4 are held at 0 V, causing TR_3 to switch off and TR_4 to switch on. The voltage at point X is therefore at 0 V. The voltage at the base of TR_2 is 0 V. Therefore TR_2 is switched off, and hence the voltage at point B is at 3 V. The high voltage at B causes TR_5 to switch on and TR_6 to switch off. The voltage at point Y is therefore at 3 V. If input 1 is connected to 0 V and input 2 to 3 V, point X is at 3 V and point Y is at 0 V, which causes the motor to reverse its direction of rotation.

The capacitors in the circuit help to remove any voltage spikes which occur. The four diodes protect the transistors from any back e.m.f. generated by the motor.

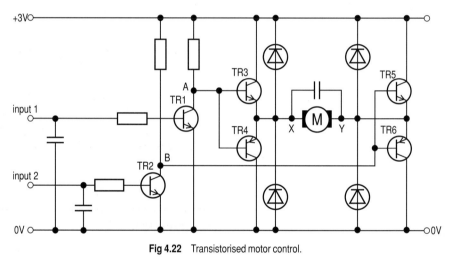

Fig 4.22 Transistorised motor control.

SUMMARY

An input device provides a voltage which is related to a physical condition.

The output voltage from a potential divider circuit is:

$$V_{OUT} = \frac{R_2}{R_1 + R_2} V_{IN}$$

A transducer changes energy from one form to another.

The resistance of an LDR decreases as light intensity increases.

The resistance of a n.t.c. thermistor decreases as temperature increases.

The resistance of a strain gauge increases when it is strained by a tensile force.

A relay is a switch operated by a small current which can control a current. A protection diode is required if the relay is being driven from an electronic circuit.

---

* The text relating to Fig 4.22 is taken from *Everyday with Practical Electronics*, January 1996.

Theme 2

DIGITAL SYSTEMS

Real-world physical quantities such as light intensity, temperature, sound or moisture are infinitely variable and, within limits, can take any value. However, decisions that are made about these quantities often result in just two outcomes: yes or no, true or false, on or off, etc. For example, we are not concerned with the exact measure of light intensity in a room to decide whether or not to switch a lamp on. Voltage signals which represent the outcome of such a decision have only a limited number of possible values, usually two, and are referred to as *digital signals*.

The theory behind digital electronics came many years before it was put into practice when George Boole, in 1847, invented a branch of mathematics which had a number base 2; in other words, the minimum number of basic quantities, which could be 1 or 0, on or off, high or low, and so on. He invented a complete shorthand method of writing down logic statements and combinations. Boole's discovery was left in the archives because there was no application for it, until, that is, the 1930s when the New York telephone system was developing so rapidly that there was no easy way to keep track of it until Claude Shannon stumbled across Boole's invention and applied it successfully to the problem; the on/off relays of the telephone exchange system being the binary base. The computer age started using the same method and Boolean algebra is now used exclusively in the digital two-state world.

The 'and', 'or' and 'not' logic operations formulated by Boole were soon translated into electronic functions called gates, and once integrated circuits were produced as ready-made 'gates' the digital computer found its way rapidly into industry and into the home.

The electronic synthesiser is capable of mimicking the sounds produced by most traditional musical instruments and combining two or more of these sounds. The keyboard has a memory bank in which the recorded sounds of actual musical instruments are stored in digital form. Only one note is stored for each instrument, but logic circuits are used to process the note to produce the desired frequency. It is popular with rock, 'pop' and jazz musicians, and is also used by composers and students of music.

5

LOGIC GATE SYSTEMS

LEARNING OBJECTIVES

After studying this chapter you should be able to:

1. convert from decimal to binary;

2. recall the truth tables for logic gates and draw their symbols;

3. use an LED as a logic state indicator;

4. recall the Boolean expressions for logic gates;

5. use Boolean algebra and the associated laws to minimise Boolean expressions;

6. recall how these gates can be made from NAND gates only;

7. apply combinational logic to decoding and arithmetic circuits.

5.1 ANALOGUE AND DIGITAL SIGNALS

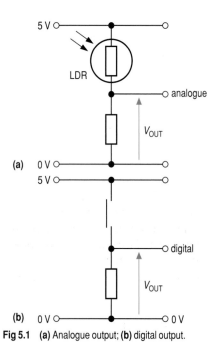

Fig 5.1 **(a)** Analogue output; **(b)** digital output.

If the LDR in the light-sensing unit of Fig 5.1(a) is made very dark and then is well illuminated, it is possible for the output voltage to rise from almost 0 V to almost 5 V (i.e. to switch from low to high or from logic 0 to logic 1). In practice, the change in illumination of the LDR is not simply just light or dark and the output signal from the light-sensing unit can have any one of a range of voltages between 0 V and 5 V. The signal from the light-sensing unit is an **analogue signal**.

If the LDR is replaced with a push-to-make switch as in Fig 5.1(b) the results obtained for this circuit are as shown in Table 5.1. This is an example of a **digital signal**. The output can only have one of two states: 0 V (logic 0 or low) or +5 V (logic 1 or high).

Table 5.1 Example of digital output

Switch	V_{out}/V
Released	0
Pressed	5

5.2 BINARY SYSTEM

Digital systems process digital signals and usually use only two numbers, **0** and **1**. Counting with just these two numbers requires the **binary system** (Table 5.2) which counts in powers of 2. The everyday decimal system counts in powers of 10. The binary number 101 is equal to the decimal number 5. Each

---

Table 5.2 The binary system of counting

2^2	2^1	2^0	Decimal
0	0	0	0
0	0	1	1
0	1	0	2
0	1	1	3
1	0	0	4
1	0	1	5
1	1	0	6
1	1	1	7

0 or 1 in a binary number is called a **bit** (**b**inary dig**it**). The binary numbers in Table 5.2 contain three bits: 101 is a three-bit number. The right-hand digit is called the **least-significant bit** (**LSB**) and the left-hand digit is called the **most-significant bit** (**MSB**).

Converting binary to decimal

We will convert two binary numbers, 110 and 1101, to decimal:

$$\text{binary } 110 = (1 \times 2^2) + (1 \times 2^1) + (0 \times 2^0)$$
$$= 4 + 2 + 0$$
$$= 6 \text{ (decimal)}$$

$$\text{binary } 1101 = (1 \times 2^3) + (1 \times 2^2) + (0 \times 2^1) + (1 \times 2^0)$$
$$= 8 + 4 + 0 + 1$$
$$= 13 \text{ (decimal)}$$

Converting decimal to binary

Repeatedly divide the number by 2 and record the remainder after each division. The remainders are either 1 or 0 and form the binary number. The example that follows shows how to convert the decimal number 13 into binary:

$$13 \div 2 = 6 \text{ remainder } \quad 1$$
$$6 \div 2 = 3 \text{ remainder } \quad 0$$
$$3 \div 2 = 1 \text{ remainder } \quad 1$$
$$1 \div 2 = 0 \text{ remainder } \quad 1$$

$$13 \text{ (decimal)} = \quad 1101 \text{ (binary)}$$

QUESTIONS

5.1 Convert these binary numbers to decimal:

(a) 1111, (b) 0001 0000, (c) 0001 0011, (d) 0001 1111, (e) 0010 0101.

5.2 Write these decimal numbers in binary form:
(a) 5, (b) 21, (c) 68, (d) 136, (e) 254.

5.3 LOGIC GATES

Logic gate symbols
For design work and block diagrams use the standard box symbol (e.g. Fig. 5.2).

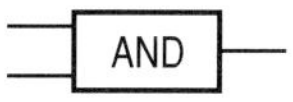

Fig 5.2 The standard box symbol for an AND gate.

The basic building blocks of digital systems such as calculators, computers and control circuits are **logic gates**. Logic gates are **decision-making** process blocks which perform particular logic functions summarised in **truth tables**. A and B represent the inputs to a gate and Q the output. A, B and Q can have one of two values: logic 1 or logic 0. The symbols used throughout this book are the American standard symbols, which are more commonly used than the British (BS) logic symbols. We now list the symbols, truth tables and functions of the logic gates.

AND gate

A	B	Q
0	0	0
0	1	0
1	0	0
1	1	1

The AND gate (Fig 5.3) gives an output of logic 1 when all its inputs are at logic 1.

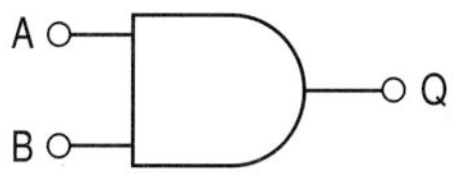

Fig 5.3 Symbol and truth table for AND gate.

OR gate

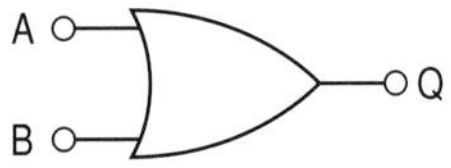

A	B	Q
0	0	0
0	1	1
1	0	1
1	1	1

The OR gate (Fig 5.4) gives an output of logic 1 when any or all of its inputs are at logic 1.

Fig 5.4   Symbol and truth table for OR gate.

NAND gate

A	B	Q
0	0	1
0	1	1
1	0	1
1	1	0

The NAND gate (Fig 5.5) gives an output of logic 0 when all inputs are at logic 1, i.e. the opposite of AND.

Fig 5.5   Symbol and truth table for NAND gate.

NOR gate

A	B	Q
0	0	1
0	1	0
1	0	0
1	1	0

The NOR gate (Fig 5.6) gives an output of logic 0 if any or both of its inputs are at logic 1, i.e. the opposite of OR.

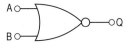

Fig 5.6   Symbol and truth table for NOR gate.

Exclusive-OR (EX-OR) gate

A	B	Q
0	0	0
0	1	1
1	0	1
1	1	0

The exclusive-OR gate (Fig 5.7) gives an output of logic 0 when all its inputs are at logic 0 or all inputs are at logic 1.

Fig 5.7   Symbol and truth table for EX-OR gate.

Exclusive-NOR (EX-NOR) gate

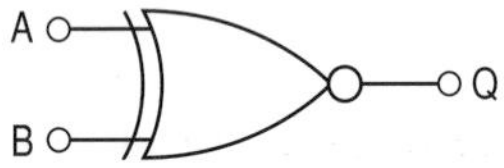

A	B	Q
0	0	1
0	1	0
1	0	0
1	1	1

The exclusive-NOR gate (Fig 5.8) gives an output of logic 1 when all inputs are at logic 0 or all inputs are at logic 1, i.e. the opposite of exclusive-OR.

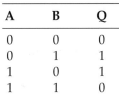

Fig 5.8   Symbol and truth table for EX-NOR gate.

Inverter or NOT gate

A	Q
0	1
1	0

The inverter or NOT gate (Fig 5.9) gives an output signal which is the **inverse** (opposite or complement) of the input.

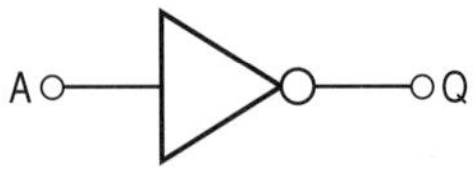

Fig 5.9   Symbol and truth table for NOT gate.

Number of inputs

Inversion symbol
The circle shown on the output of some gates indicates the inversion function.

An inverter only has one input. AND, OR and NAND gates can have two or more inputs. Exclusive-OR and exclusive-NOR gates have two inputs.

LOGIC GATE SYSTEMS

Fig 5.10 shows the symbol and truth table for a three-input AND gate.

A	B	C	Q
0	0	0	0
0	0	1	0
0	1	0	0
0	1	1	0
1	0	0	0
1	0	1	0
1	1	0	0
1	1	1	1

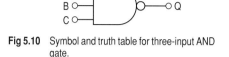

Fig 5.10 Symbol and truth table for three-input AND gate.

5.4 USING LOGIC ICs

Logic gate integrated circuits are classified according to the semiconductor technology used in their manufacture. The two basic logic families are **CMOS** (complementary metal oxide semiconductor) and **TTL** (transistor transistor logic). Each of these is then divided into sub-families.

- *74-series* The most common family of logic devices is known as the 74-series. ICs from this family are coded with the prefix number 74. Sub-families are identified by letters which follow this prefix. Some of these are identified in Table 5.3.

Table 5.3 The 74-series ICs

Code	Meaning	Notes
None	The original TTL	Used in basic circuits where speed and power consumption are not important
LS	Low-power Schottky	Consumes only 20% of the power that an original 74 IC does
C	CMOS version of a TTL IC	
HC	High-speed CMOS	CMOS-compatible inputs
HCT	High-speed CMOS	TTL-compatible inputs

- *4000-series* The most common family of CMOS ICs is known as the 4000-series.

The characteristics of common TTL and CMOS logic ICs are detailed in Appendix B. The circuits described in this book assume the use of CMOS 74HC devices.

Important practical notes for CMOS ICs

⚠

All unused inputs must be connected to 0 V or to +5 V otherwise erratic behaviour may occur.

CMOS ICs can be damaged by static charge; keep ICs within their protective anti-static packaging when not in use, and wear an anti-static wristband which is connected to Earth.

The power supply range for the 74HC series is 2–6 V.

LED logic indicators

LEDs are often used in digital circuits to indicate a logic state. The following investigation enables you to test the function of a logic gate using an LED. The output current of a 74HC gate is about 20 mA (compared with 1 mA for CMOS 4000B series) which is sufficient to drive standard LEDs, but the use of low-current LEDs as indicators, together with 1 kΩ series resistors, ensures that there is sufficient current available to drive subsequent gates. All the investigations described in the book assume the use of low-current LEDs.

Low-current LED
The intensity of low-current LEDs remains constant down to 2 mA.

The behaviour of logic gates

Apparatus: 5 V (or 6 V) regulated power supply; a breadboard; low-current LEDs; 1 kΩ resistors; certain specified logic ICs.

(a) To examine the behaviour of a single gate

A 74HC00 IC contains four NAND gates. The connections to its 14 pins (terminals) are shown in Fig 5.11(a). Connect pin 14 to +5 V and pin 7 to 0 V. These connections are needed to supply power to the IC. The NAND gate being used has inputs on pins 9 and 10 and an output on pin 8. This output is connected to the 0 V through an LED and a 1 kΩ resistor (Fig 5.11(b)). Free wire leads can be used for the inputs.

Connect the free leads to 0 V. The truth table for the NAND gate indicates that this should give a logic 1 output so the LED should light. Then transfer one or other of the leads from 0 V to +5 V; the LED should still light. Then connect both leads to +5 V, the LED should go out.

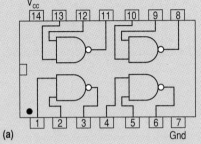

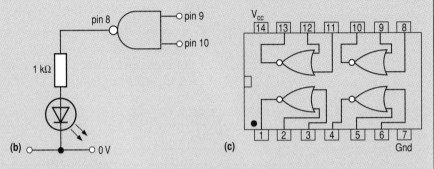

(a)

Fig 5.11 The pin connections for logic ICs: **(a)** pin diagram for 74HC00; **(b)** pin connections for test circuit; **(c)** pin diagram for 74HC02.

Now connect the LED to the output of a NOR gate (the pin diagram is shown in Fig 5.11(c)). How must you connect the input leads to make the LED light?

(b) Combinations of gates

You should now be able to use any combination of gates, but to start it is suggested that you use all four gates on a 74HC00 IC in the combination shown in Fig 5.12. Before you start this experimentally, work out what you expect in the truth table. To do this, work through the table in the sequence shown. To find C, you should use A and B as inputs; to find D, you should use C and A as inputs, etc. Q is the output from the circuit which can be connected to an LED, but you could, if you so desired, connect LEDs at C and D and E also. Each LED must have its own series resistor.

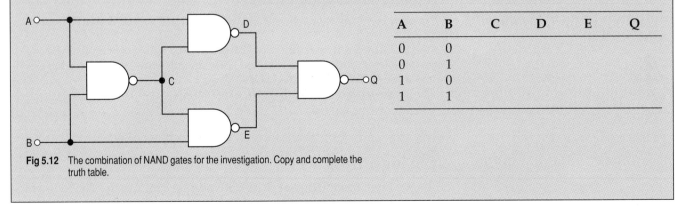

A	B	C	D	E	Q
0	0				
0	1				
1	0				
1	1				

Fig 5.12 The combination of NAND gates for the investigation. Copy and complete the truth table.

When embarking on project work involving logic gates, kits are useful tools for developing your solution. Computer software such as 'Crocodile Clips' illustrated in Fig 5.13 is also available with which you can create animated logic circuits.

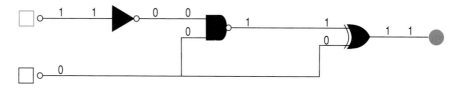

Fig 5.13 Software such as 'Crocodile Clips' runs on Microsoft Windows 3.1.

Individually, logic gates have limited use, but it is possible to link them together in ways which enable a multitude of different functions to be performed. A computer uses thousands of linked gates. The output of one gate is connected to the input of another and the process can be continued almost indefinitely.

5.5 COMBINATIONS OF LOGIC GATES

Fig 5.14 shows how logic gates can be combined to perform a particular function, summarised by a truth table.

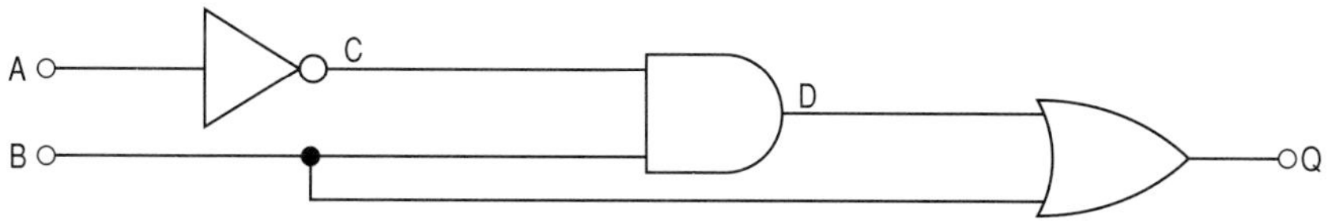

A	B	C	D	Q
0	0	1	0	0
0	1	1	1	1
1	0	0	0	0
1	1	0	0	1

Fig 5.14 This combination of logic gates will perform the particular function summarised in the truth table.

In this example the output Q is at logic 1 when A is **NOT** at logic 1 **AND** B is at logic 1 **OR** when A **AND** B are at logic 1. This statement of the function of this circuit can be shortened using Boolean logic. The Boolean expression for this combination of logic gates is

$$Q = \overline{A}.B + A.B$$

which is read as output is equal to NOT A AND B OR A AND B.

5.6 BOOLEAN LOGIC

Combining logic gates to perform complex functions can prove very difficult particularly when dealing with computer logic. This task can be simplified by applying Boolean algebra, named after the English mathematician George Boole who, in 1847, invented a shorthand method of writing down combinations of logic statements.

Table 5.4 shows the Boolean expressions for logic gates.

The inputs A, B and output Q represent the **Boolean variables** which can only be logic 1 or logic 0.

A **bar** over a letter such as $\overline{A}$ means **NOT A**, so if A is 1, $\overline{A}$ is 0 and if A is 0, $\overline{A}$ is 1. A and $\overline{A}$ are said to be **complementary states**.

Looking back at the truth tables for the logic gates, it should be apparent that the statements in Table 5.5 apply to AND and OR functions.

Table 5.4 Boolean expressions for logic gates

Gate	Symbol	Boolean expression
NOT		$Q = \overline{A}$
AND		$Q = A.B$
OR		$Q = A + B$
NAND		$Q = \overline{A.B}$
NOR		$Q = \overline{A + B}$
EX-OR		$Q = A \oplus B$
EX-NOR		$Q = \overline{A \oplus B}$

Use of '+' and '.'
Note that **A + B** represents the **OR** function and **A.B** represents the **AND** function.

Table 5.5   AND and OR functions

AND	OR
$A.0 = 0$	$A + 0 = A$
$A.1 = A$	$A + 1 = 1$
$A.A = A$	$A + A = A$
$A.\overline{A} = 0$	$A + \overline{A} = 1$
$\overline{A}.A = 0$	$\overline{A} + 1 = 1$

Example: For the logic gate combination shown in Fig 5.15, the output Q is at logic 1 when A **OR** B is at logic 1 **AND** C is at logic 1. The Boolean expression for this combination is **Q = (A + B).C**. (The brackets define the order in which the operations are performed.) The truth table is also shown in the figure.

A	B	C	(A + B)	(A + B).C
0	0	0	0	0
0	0	1	0	0
0	1	0	1	0
0	1	1	1	1
1	0	0	1	0
1	0	1	1	1
1	1	0	1	0
1	1	1	1	1

Fig 5.15   Logic gate combination and truth table for the example.

QUESTION

5.3 Write down the Boolean expression for the combination of logic gates shown in Fig 5.16.

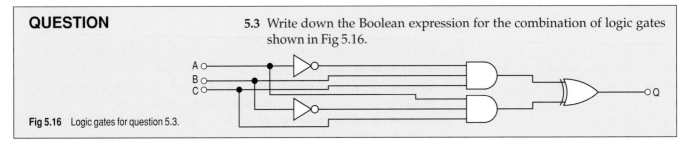

Fig 5.16   Logic gates for question 5.3.

Expressions for EX-OR and EX-NOR

Useful Boolean expressions can be written for EX-OR and EX-NOR gates by considering their truth tables.

The output of an EX-OR gate is equal to (NOT A AND B) OR (A AND NOT B):

$$A \oplus B = \overline{A}.B + A.\overline{B}$$

The output of an EX-NOR gate is equal to (NOT A AND NOT B) OR (A AND B):

$$\overline{A \oplus B} = \overline{A}.\overline{B} + A.B$$

Simplifying expressions

A useful property of Boolean operations is that more than one combination of gates will produce the same result. This means that Boolean algebra can be used to simplify an expression to enable you to use the minimum number of logic gates in your design. This is preferred because it reduces the cost and power consumption and increases the speed of operation.

To simplify Boolean expressions you need to know the following laws of Boolean algebra:

De Morgan's laws
- First law

$$\overline{A + B} = \overline{A}.\overline{B}$$

- Second law

$$\overline{A.B} = \overline{A} + \overline{B}$$

These laws can easily be proved by writing out the truth table for both sides of each equation as in Table 5.6. Column [4] is the same as column [7], which proves the first of De Morgan's laws. Prove the second law for yourself.

Table 5.6   Proving De Morgan's first law using a truth table

Left-hand side of equation				Right-hand side of equation		
A	B	A+B	$\overline{A + B}$	$\overline{A}$	$\overline{B}$	$\overline{A}.\overline{B}$
0	0	0	1	1	1	1
0	1	1	0	1	0	0
1	0	1	0	0	1	0
1	1	1	0	0	0	0
[1]	[2]	[3]	[4]	[5]	[6]	[7]

Other laws
Other laws associated with Boolean algebra are the following:
- Double inversion

$$\overline{\overline{A}} = A$$

- Commutative laws

$$A + B = B + A$$
$$A.B = B.A$$

- Associative laws

$$A + (B + C) = (A + B) + C$$
$$A.(B.C) = (A.B).C$$

- Distributive laws

$$A.(B + C) = (A.B) + (A.C)$$
$$A + (B.C) = (A + B).(A + C)$$

- Product of sums
  $(A + B).(A + B) = A.A + A.B + B.A + B.B$

Any of these laws can be proved in the same way as we proved De Morgan's theory.

Redundancy theorem
In a Boolean expression containing a sum of products, a product that contains all the factors of another product is redundant. For example,

$$A.B + A.B.C + A.B.D = A.B$$

The terms A.B.C and A.B.D can be eliminated because each contains factors present in A.B

QUESTION

5.4 Show, using a truth table, that $A.B + A.\overline{B} = A$.

The redundancy theorem is used to reduce the amount of circuitry involved in the implementation of logic functions.

The following examples show how the laws of Boolean algebra can be used together to simplify expressions in an attempt to minimise the number of gates used.

Example 1: Fig 5.17 shows a combination of logic gates. Its Boolean expression is

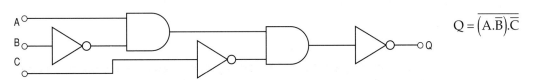

$$Q = \overline{\left(A.\overline{B}\right).\overline{C}}$$

Fig 5.17 Combination of logic gates for example 1.

Using the simplification laws we obtain

$$
\begin{aligned}
Q &= \overline{\left(A.\overline{B}\right).\overline{C}} \\
&= \overline{A.\left(\overline{B.\overline{C}}\right)} && \text{associative law} \\
&= \overline{A.\overline{B} + C} && \text{De Morgan's first law} \\
&= \overline{A} + \overline{\left(\overline{B} + C\right)} && \text{De Morgan's second law} \\
&= \overline{A} + \left(B + C\right) && \text{double inversion}
\end{aligned}
$$

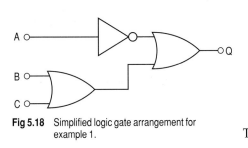

Fig 5.18 Simplified logic gate arrangement for example 1.

The simplified logic circuit is shown in Fig 5.18.

QUESTION

5.5 Write out the Boolean expression for the gate combination shown in Fig 5.19 and construct its truth table. Simplify the expression to prove that $Q = B.\overline{A}$ and draw the simplified gate circuit and construct its truth table to verify that you have the correct expression.

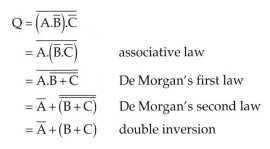

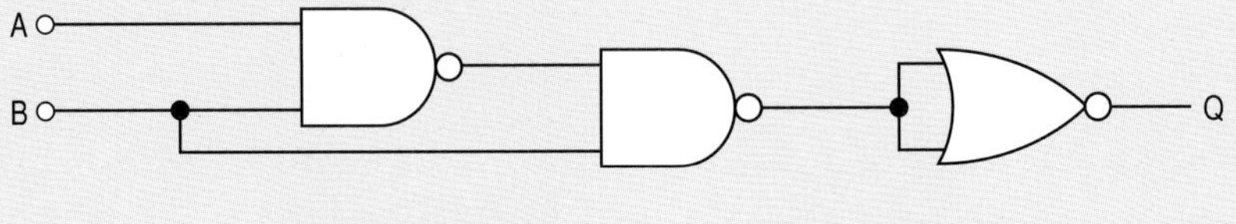

Fig 5.19 Combination of logic gates for question 5.5.

Example 2: Show that $(A + B).(A + \overline{B}) = A$

$$(A + B).(A + \overline{B}) = A.A + B.A \; + \; A.\overline{B} + B.\overline{B}$$
$$= A + B.A + A.\overline{B} + 0$$
$$= A.(1 + B) + A.\overline{B} + 0$$
$$= A.1 + A.\overline{B} + 0$$
$$= A + A.B$$
$$= A.(1 + B)$$
$$= A.1$$
$$= A$$

QUESTION **5.6** Show that $\overline{(A + B).(\overline{B}.A)} = B + \overline{A}$.

5.7 THE 'UNIVERSAL' NAND GATE

'Universal' NOR?
NOR gates can also be used to produce all logic functions but NAND version is the industry standard.

Since logic ICs generally contain four two-input logic gates it makes sense to use as many of these as possible. For example, if your circuit requires an inverter and an OR gate, you could use the 74HC04 and 74HC32 ICs but would only be using one gate from each. Alternatively, you could construct both gates from a single NAND IC, i.e. 74HC00. This is because all logic functions can be constructed from NAND gates alone. The advantage of this is a reduction in the number of ICs needed in a circuit.

Inverter

The inputs of the gate (Fig 5.20) are connected together so the input can only have two states: A = B = 0, A = B = 1. This is the truth table for a NOT gate.

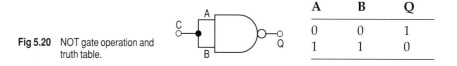

A	B	Q
0	0	1
1	1	0

Fig 5.20 NOT gate operation and truth table.

AND gate

If a NAND gate is inverted then the combination has the same function as the AND gate (Fig 5.21).

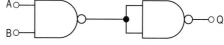

Fig 5.21 AND gate operation.

OR gate

OR function using De Morgan's laws

$$\overline{A + B} = \overline{A}.\overline{B}$$
$$\overline{\overline{A + B}} = \overline{\overline{A}.\overline{B}}$$
$$A + B = \overline{\overline{A}.\overline{B}}$$

This is a more complex arrangement to remember than the above, but De Morgan's theory can be used to determine the correct arrangement of NAND gates to make an OR gate. Using De Morgan's first law it can be shown that $A + B = \overline{\overline{A}.\overline{B}}$. This gives us the circuit in Fig 5.22. The truth table for this circuit is also shown. Fig 5.23 is the equivalent circuit using NAND gates only.

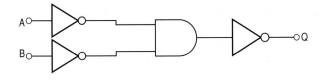

Fig 5.22 OR gate operation and truth table.

A	B	$\overline{A}$	$\overline{B}$	$\overline{A}.\overline{B}$	$\overline{\overline{A}.\overline{B}}$
0	0	1	1	1	0
0	1	1	0	0	1
1	0	0	1	0	1
1	1	0	0	0	1

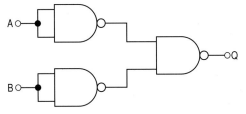

Fig 5.23 OR gate operation using only NAND gates.

NOR gate

This is shown in Fig 5.24.

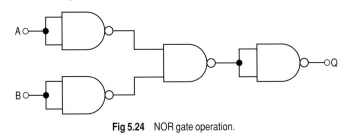

Fig 5.24 NOR gate operation.

EX-OR gate

It is difficult to work out the equivalent NAND gate circuit for the EX-OR gate (Fig 5.25), but once given you can check it with a truth table. The Boolean notation for the circuit in Fig 5.25 is $\overline{\overline{A.\overline{A.B}}.\overline{B.\overline{A.B}}}$. This can be simplified as follows:

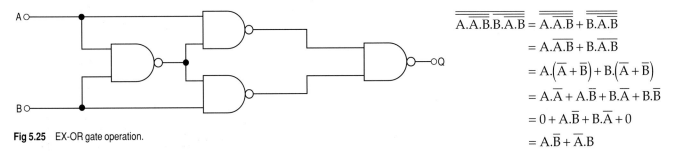

Fig 5.25 EX-OR gate operation.

$$\overline{\overline{A.\overline{A.B}}.\overline{B.\overline{A.B}}} = \overline{\overline{A.\overline{A.B}}} + \overline{\overline{B.\overline{A.B}}}$$
$$= A.\overline{A.B} + B.\overline{A.B}$$
$$= A.(\overline{A}+\overline{B}) + B.(\overline{A}+\overline{B})$$
$$= A.\overline{A} + A.\overline{B} + B.\overline{A} + B.\overline{B}$$
$$= 0 + A.\overline{B} + B.\overline{A} + 0$$
$$= A.\overline{B} + \overline{A}.B$$

where $A.\overline{B} + \overline{A}.B$ is the Boolean notation for the EX-OR function.

QUESTION   5.7 What is the equivalent NAND gate circuit for the EX-NOR gate?

The circuits considered so far can be described as **combinational** logic circuits where the output is determined only by the current states of the various inputs. The use of combinational logic in **decoder** and **arithmetic** circuits is described in the following sections. **Sequential** logic systems are discussed in Chapter 7.

5.8 DECODING

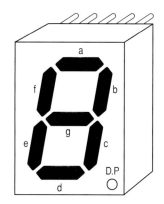

Fig 5.26 Seven-segment display.

Seven-segment displays enable numbers (0 to 9) and some letters to be displayed. One of the most common types of display uses light-emitting diodes. The arrangement of the LED segments in a typical display is shown in Fig 5.26. The segments are identified by the letters a to g. Two configurations of segments are available, common-anode and common-cathode, depending on which segment connection is connected to a common point. Fig 5.27 shows the connections to a common-cathode display. A series resistor is required for each segment of the display to limit the forward current to typically 20 mA. A segment is illuminated by connecting a forward voltage across it. The number or letter displayed depends on which segments are illuminated. Decoder circuits facilitate the process of illuminating the correct segments. To express the numbers 0 to 9 in binary requires a four-bit binary number which must be **decoded** into seven bits to operate the seven segments of the display. For example, to display the number 8, the binary number 1000 must be processed into the pattern 1111111 to ensure that all of the segments are energised.

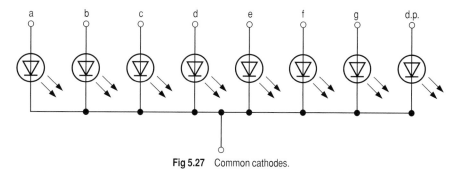

Fig 5.27 Common cathodes.

Decoding systems can be constructed from logic ICs. A basic one to consider first is the **two-line to four-line** (or two-bit to four-bit) decoder shown in Fig 5.28.

Inputs		Outputs			
A_1	A_0	d	c	b	a
0	0	0	0	0	1
0	1	0	0	1	0
1	0	0	1	0	0
1	1	1	0	0	0

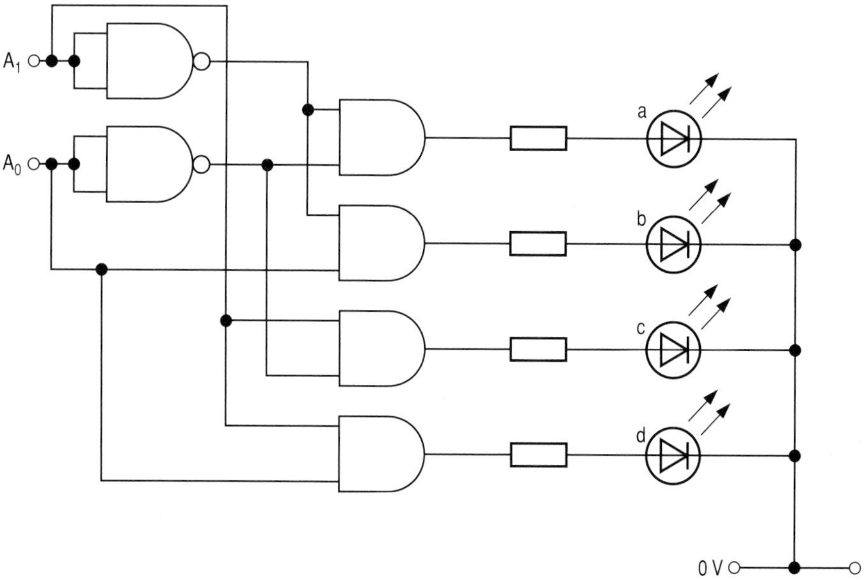

Fig 5.28 Two-bit to four-bit decoder circuit and truth table.

Integrated circuits are available specifically to drive an LED display from a four-bit counter. The 74HC4543 is a **binary-coded decimal (BCD) to seven-segment decoder driver**. It contains the necessary logic gate arrangements to ensure that the correct segments are illuminated for each input code. Refer to the system of lettering of the display in Fig 5.26 to understand how the four-bit binary number is converted into seven bits to operate each segment of the display (Table 5.7). A_0, A_1, etc., are the usual notation for the inputs to decoder ICs; these inputs connect to Q_0, Q_1, etc., the outputs of the counter.

Table 5.7   Decoding the four-bit input into the seven bits needed to drive the display

Inputs from counter				Outputs							Display
A_3	A_2	A_1	A_0	a	b	c	d	e	f	g	
0	0	0	0	1	1	1	1	1	1	0	*0*
0	0	0	1	0	1	1	0	0	0	0	*1*
0	0	1	0	1	1	0	1	1	0	1	*2*
etc.				etc.							etc.

QUESTION

5.8 Copy and complete Table 5.7 to show the logic states for the inputs and outputs of the decoder up to display *9*.

5.9 BINARY ARITHMETIC

Calculators and computer systems manipulate binary numbers using circuits that can add and subtract. The addition of binary numbers using logic gates is described in this section.

- Rules for binary arithmetic

$$0 + 0 = 0$$
$$0 + 1 = 1$$
$$1 + 0 = 1$$
$$1 + 1 = 0 \quad \text{carry 1}$$
$$1 + 1 + 1 = 1 \quad \text{carry 1}$$

A circuit which adds two binary bits is called a **half-adder**. A truth table can be used to determine the logic gates required to perform this addition. Table 5.8 shows the truth table for a circuit which adds two bits A and B. The Boolean notation is:

$$\text{sum} = A \oplus B$$

$$\text{carry} = A.B$$

A half-adder can be constructed from an AND gate and an exclusive-OR gate as shown in Fig 5.29.

Table 5.8   Truth table for a half-adder

A	B	Sum	Carry
0	0	0	0
0	1	1	0
1	0	1	0
1	1	0	1

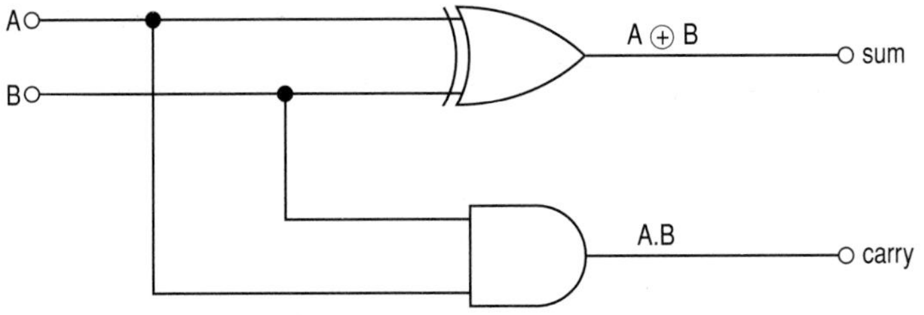

Fig 5.29   Half-adder.

A **full-adder** circuit can add three bits at a time and therefore is able to add a carry from a previous stage to the sum of the inputs A and B. Table 5.9 shows the truth table for a full-adder circuit.

Table 5.9 Truth table for a full-adder

A	B	C (carry in)	Sum	Carry (carry out)
0	0	0	0	0
0	0	1	1	0
0	1	0	1	0
0	1	1	0	1
1	0	0	1	0
1	0	1	0	1
1	1	0	0	1
1	1	1	1	1

The Boolean expressions for EX-OR and EX-NOR can be written as:

$$\text{EX - OR :} \quad A \oplus B = \overline{A}.B + A.\overline{B}$$

$$\text{EX - NOR :} \quad \overline{A \oplus B} = \overline{A}.\overline{B} + A.B$$

These can be used to determine the logic circuit for a full-adder.

From the truth table in Table 5.9, the simplest expressions for the sum and carry operations can be written as:

$$\text{sum} = \overline{A}.\overline{B}.C + \overline{A}.B.\overline{C} + A.\overline{B}.\overline{C} + A.B.C$$

$$\text{carry} = \overline{A}.B.C + A.\overline{B}.C + A.B.\overline{C} + A.B.C$$

These expressions can be minimised using Boolean algebra as shown below:

$$\text{sum} = \overline{A}.\overline{B}.C + \overline{A}.B.\overline{C} + A.\overline{B}.\overline{C} + A.B.C$$
$$= C.\left(\overline{A}.\overline{B} + A.B\right) + \overline{C}.\left(\overline{A}.B + A.\overline{B}\right)$$
$$= C.\left(\overline{A \oplus B}\right) + \overline{C}.\left(A \oplus B\right)$$
$$= C \oplus \left(A \oplus B\right)$$

$$\text{carry} = \overline{A}.B.C + A.\overline{B}.C + A.B.\overline{C} + A.B.C$$
$$= \overline{A}.B.C + A.\overline{B}.C + A.B.\left(\overline{C} + C\right)$$
$$= C.\left(\overline{A}.B + A.\overline{B}\right) + A.B$$
$$= C.\left(A \oplus B\right) + A.B$$

The full-adder circuit is shown in Fig 5.30.

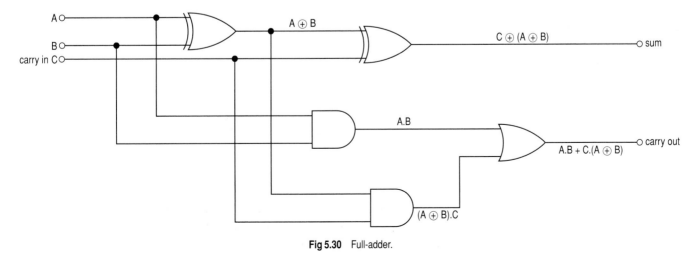

Fig 5.30 Full-adder.

SUMMARY

The numbers 0 and 1 are used in binary counting. Each number in a binary pattern is called a bit.

Truth tables and symbols for logic gates:

One input gate

NOT gate	
Input	Output
0	1
1	0

Two input gates

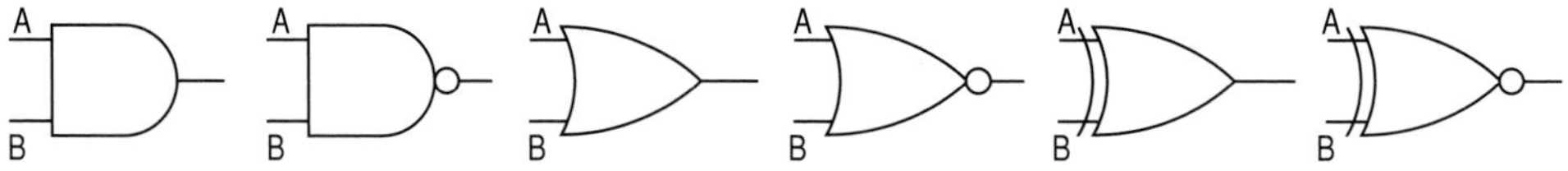

Inputs		AND	NAND	OR	NOR	EX-OR	EX-NOR
A	B						
0	0	0	1	0	1	0	1
0	1	0	1	1	0	1	0
1	0	0	1	1	0	1	0
1	1	1	0	1	0	0	1

Boolean expressions:

Gate	Boolean expression
NOT	$Q = \overline{A}$
AND	$Q = A.B$
OR	$Q = A + B$
NAND	$Q = \overline{A.B}$
NOR	$Q = \overline{A + B}$
EX-OR	$Q = A \oplus B$
EX-NOR	$Q = \overline{A \oplus B}$

De Morgan's laws:

$$\text{first law} \quad \overline{A + B} = \overline{A}.\overline{B}$$
$$\text{second law} \quad \overline{A.B} = \overline{A} + \overline{B}$$

All logic gates can be constructed from NAND gates only.

Applications of combinational logic: decoding and binary arithmetic.

Chapter 6

TIMING SYSTEMS

LEARNING OBJECTIVES

After studying this chapter you should be able to:

1. state the function and uses of astable and monostable circuits;

2. recall how to construct monostable and astable circuits using logic gates and the 555 timer IC, and estimate the time period by calculation;

3. understand the terms 'mark-time', 'space-time', 'period', 'frequency' and 'amplitude' and use a CRO to measure them.

6.1 TIMING SYSTEMS

On a pedestrian crossing (Fig 6.1) the 'green man' comes on for about 15 seconds, which indicates that it is safe to cross the road. The 'green man' will then flash on and off for a short time to warn pedestrians not to cross. The system uses a **monostable** circuit to produce a fixed time period that the 'man' is illuminated, and an **astable** circuit to enable the 'man' to pulse on and off. These circuits are often called **multivibrators**.

Fig 6.1 A pedestrian crossing system makes use of monostable and astable circuits.

There are many different ways of constructing monostable and astable circuits; this chapter looks at logic gates and 555 timer IC circuits. Resistors and capacitors are the main external components of any timing system.

The timing circuit

The *RC* network (Fig 6.2) used in logic gate monostable circuits is often called a **differentiator** circuit. You will recall from Chapter 2 that the time it takes for

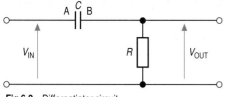

Fig 6.2 Differentiator circuit.

a capacitor to discharge through a resistor is determined by the time constant. The relationship between the voltage across the capacitor and time for discharge is given by the equation:

$$V = V_0 e^{-t/CR}$$

This formula can be used to determine the time it takes for the voltage across the capacitor to fall to half its original value. This is called the **half-life**, $t_{1/2}$. When $t = t_{1/2}$, $V = \frac{1}{2}V_0$, so the above equation gives

$$\frac{1}{2}V_0 = V_0 e^{-t_{1/2}/CR}$$

$$\frac{1}{2} = e^{-t_{1/2}/CR}$$

Taking natural logarithms of both sides of this equation:

$$\ln 0.5 = -\frac{t_{1/2}}{CR}$$

$$0.693 = \frac{t_{1/2}}{CR}$$

$$t_{1/2} = 0.693CR$$

Therefore we get

$$t_{1/2} \approx 0.7CR$$

where $t_{1/2}$ is the half-life in seconds, C is the capacitance in farads and R is the resistance in ohms.

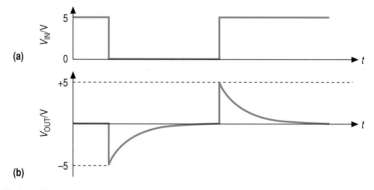

Fig 6.3 Waveforms in the differentiator circuit: **(a)** applied voltage; **(b)** p.d. across the resistor.

If a pulse as shown in Fig 6.3(a) is applied to the RC circuit in Fig 6.2, the output waveform across the resistor exhibits negative and positive spikes as in Fig 6.3(b). Suppose that the capacitor is fully charged and that the p.d. across it is 5 V. When V_{IN} falls abruptly to 0 V, there is no time for any charge to flow off the plates of the capacitor, so the p.d. across the capacitor must remain at 5 V. Plate A is at 0 V so, in order for the p.d. to remain the same, the potential of plate B must be –5 V at the instant plate A is pushed from +5 V to 0 V. There is now a p.d. across the resistor causing charge to flow and V_{OUT} rises up to 0 V (the time it takes to rise depends on the time constant, CR). After a time equal to 0.7CR (half-life), V_{OUT} will have risen to –2.5 V; and after a time of about 5CR, V_{OUT} will be about 0 V. If, after this time, V_{IN} rises abruptly to +5 V, V_{OUT} will also be pushed up to +5 V and will then decay back down to 0 V with a half-life of 0.7CR. If the output of the differentiator circuit was connected into a logic gate, the IC could be destroyed by the negative spikes. However, this is not the case because both CMOS and TTL gates contain an **input protection circuit** which consists of semiconducting diodes that prevent the input from falling below –0.7 V.

6.2 MONOSTABLE CIRCUITS

The **monostable** has two output states (logic 1 or logic 0) but it is only stable in one state (hence *mono*stable). When it receives a **trigger** input signal, the output is forced into the other state. It does not stay in this state, but returns to the stable state after a certain time – the **monostable period**. This time delay is controlled by a **resistor–capacitor network**.

NOR gate monostable

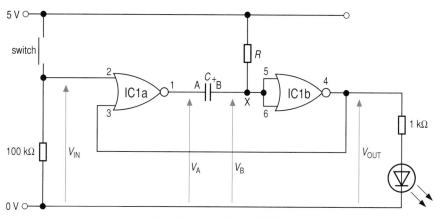

Fig 6.4   NOR gate monostable.

Fig 6.4 shows a monostable circuit constructed from NOR gates (74HC02). The trigger input is normally held at 0 V via the 100 kΩ resistor. The input is **triggered** by pressing and then releasing the switch, momentarily pulling pin 2 to 5 V. This momentary transition from logic 0 to logic 1 is referred to as a **rising edge** trigger signal. When a **trigger** signal is received at pin 2, the LED lights for a certain length of time. This **monostable period** is determined by the values of R and C.

<table>
<tr><td>

Important note about threshold voltages

</td><td>

The input voltage that gate IC1b (Fig 6.4) considers to be a logic 1 determines the level up to which the capacitor must charge in order for the monostable to change state. Nominally for CMOS ICs this **logic 0/1 threshold is half the supply voltage,** i.e. 2.5 V. The theory described is based on this assumption, and hence any formulae quoted are not totally accurate but are near enough to be of practical use.

</td></tr>
</table>

When the switch is pressed, the potential at pin 2 is 5 V (logic 1). Assuming that pin 3 (and hence the output of IC1b) is at 0 V, then the output pin 1 will switch from logic 1 to logic 0 (refer to NOR gate truth table in Fig 5.6). This voltage change is transmitted instantly by the capacitor, making pins 5 and 6 change to logic 0 and causing the output pin 4 to change state from logic 0 to logic 1 and the LED to switch on. This logic 1 voltage level is transferred back to pin 3, which ensures that the circuit remains in its new state even when the trigger switch is released. At the instant the LED switches on, there is then a p.d. across the resistor R, since the potential at point X is 0 V. The p.d. across R causes current to pass in the CR circuit and the capacitor charges up. After a time equal to $0.7CR$ (half-life) the potential at X (plate B of the capacitor) rises to 2.5 V (half the supply voltage). At this threshold voltage, the output pin 4 switches back to 0 V and the LED switches off. Pin 3 is therefore at 0 V and, provided the trigger switch has been released, pin 2 is also at 0 V, so the potential at pin 1 is +5 V. This abrupt change in potential at plate A of the capacitor from 0 V to +5 V will result in a positive voltage spike at pins 5 and 6. The p.d. across the capacitor remains the same (2.5 V) so, at this instant, the potential at plate B will be pulled up to +7.5 V. This would damage the IC, but the internal protection diodes of the IC should prevent this voltage from rising above 5.7 V.

The sequence of events is best represented by the graphs in Fig 6.5 which show how the p.d. changes at various points in the circuit.

'One-shot'
Engineers sometimes refer to the monostable as a 'one-shot' as it generates a single pulse only.

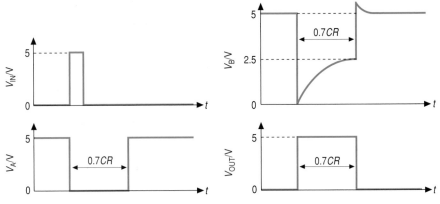

Fig 6.5 Timing diagrams for NOR gate monostable.

In summary, the NOR gate monostable is triggered by a **rising edge**. It has

monostable period $t = 0.7CR$

where t is in seconds, C in farads and R in ohms. Polarised or non-polarised capacitors can be used for C.

INVESTIGATION

The NOR gate monostable

Construct the monostable circuit shown in Fig 6.4 using a quad two-input NOR gate IC such as the 74HC02. Record the monostable period for different R and C values. Select values which will give a measurable time period and compare the actual period with the theoretical period. Why may these be different? Investigate the effect of keeping the switch closed longer than the monostable period.

NAND gate monostable

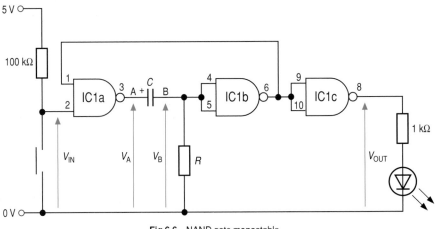

Fig 6.6   NAND gate monostable.

Fig 6.6 shows a monostable circuit constructed from NAND gates (74HC00). This NAND gate monostable circuit is similar to the NOR gate version, but responds in the opposite way.

Practical note about the use of logic ICs for multivibrator circuits

In a circuit design, it is sometimes convenient to utilise spare logic gates to provide a time delay (monostable). Whilst this might be a convenient and inexpensive solution, wherever possible dedicated monostable ICs or the 555 timer IC should be used instead of logic gates. The reason for this is the unpredictability of logic gate circuits due to the tolerances of components and the variations in logic threshold levels. (Appendix B details the guaranteed logic levels for common logic ICs.) CMOS logic ICs dislike operating in the **indeterminate zone**, the region between the guaranteed logic 0 and logic 1 levels, which may be the case when the capacitor is charging up. The use of electrolytic capacitors results in poor timing accuracy due to their high leakage current (2200 μF is the maximum value recommended). The problem is that a large-value electrolytic capacitor is needed to generate a reasonably long delay, so very often a compromise is needed between accuracy and an extended time delay. Again, for long delays, dedicated ICs are more suitable, such as the ZN1034E **precision timer**, which will provide time delays from 50 ms to several days with a typical accuracy of 0.01%. Where possible, if you are using logic gates, use unpolarised capacitors which have a low leakage current. For similar reasons, dedicated ICs or the 555 timer should be used, wherever possible, for astable circuits.

There are some advantages for using logic gate multivibrator circuits. The ICs are generally cheaper to buy than specially designed ones, particularly if you have gates available on ICs already being used in your circuit design. They can be easily interfaced with other logic circuits and draw little stand-by current, making them ideal for battery use.

6.3 ASTABLE CIRCUITS

The **astable** has two output states, but is not stable in either state, and constantly switches (or oscillates) from one state (logic 1) to the other (logic 0). An RC network determines the frequency at which the output oscillates. An astable therefore generates digital output pulses and the waveform produced is known as a **square wave** if $t_1 = t_2$ (Fig 6.7).

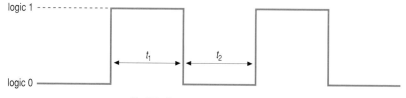

Fig 6.7   Square wave output (if $t_1 = t_2$).

We now need some definitions. The **mark-time** t_1 is the time that the output is at logic 1. The **space-time** t_2 is the time that the output is at logic 0. Also

$$\text{mark-to-space ratio} = \frac{\text{mark-time}}{\text{space-time}} = \frac{t_1}{t_2}$$

The **astable period** T is the time for one complete pulse, i.e. the time it takes for the output to change from one state to the other and back again, i.e. $T = t_1 + t_2$. The **frequency** f is the number of complete cycles it can go through in one second:

$$\text{frequency, } f = \frac{1}{\text{period, } T}$$

where f is measured in hertz (Hz) and T in seconds.

NOT gate astable

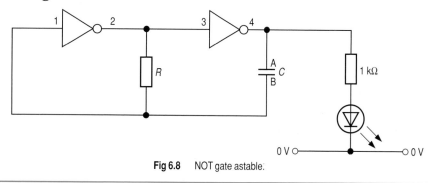

Fig 6.8   NOT gate astable.

Fig 6.8 shows an astable circuit constructed from NOT gates (74HC04). If the LED is on when the power supply to the gates is switched on, then the potential at pin 1 is high and the potential at pins 2 and 3 is low. There is a p.d. across R and therefore charging current flows and the potential of plate B of the capacitor falls. The time it takes to fall depends on the values of R and C. When the potential at B falls to 2.5 V (logic 1/0 threshold) pins 2 and 3 go high and pin 4 goes low and the LED goes off. The sudden drop in potential at A from +5 V to 0 V means a drop in potential at plate B from +2.5 V to −2.5 V (a drop of 5 V). The p.d. across R results in the charging current flowing the opposite way. (This is the reason why non-polarised capacitors are used. Polarised capacitors (electrolytic and tantalum) would be damaged.) The potential at plate B now rises and when it reaches the switching threshold voltage of 2.5 V pin 2 goes low and pin 4 goes high, and the LED is on. The sudden rise in potential at A from 0 V to +5 V means a rise in potential at plate B from 2.5 V to +7.5 V (a rise of 5 V), the direction of the charging current reverses and the process repeats itself. The time it takes for the p.d. across the capacitor to rise from −2.5 V to +2.5 V (to charge up to 67% of its final value) and to fall from 7.5 V to 2.5 V (to fall to 33% of its initial value) can be determined as follows:

- To charge up

$$V = V_0(1 - e^{-t/CR})$$

$$5 = 7.5(1 - e^{-t/CR})$$

$$0.67 = 1 - e^{-t/CR}$$

$$e^{-t/CR} = 0.33$$

$$t = -CR \ln 0.33$$

$$t = 1.1CR$$

- To fall

$$V = V_0 e^{-t/CR}$$

$$2.5 = 7.5 e^{-t/CR}$$

$$0.33 = e^{-t/CR}$$

$$e^{-t/CR} = 0.33$$

$$t = -CR \ln 0.33$$

$$t = 1.1CR$$

The sequence of events is best represented by the graphs in Fig 6.9, which show how the p.d. changes at various points in the circuit. The internal protection diodes of the IC should prevent the voltage at pin 1 from falling below 0.7 V and from rising above 5.7 V.

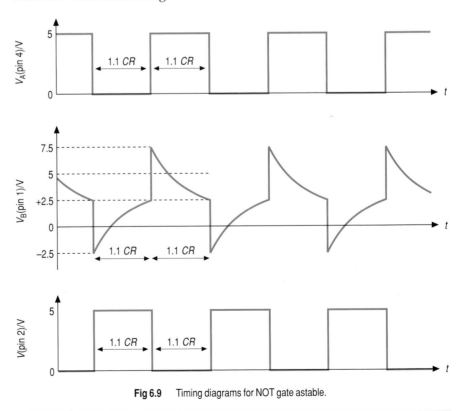

Fig 6.9 Timing diagrams for NOT gate astable.

TIMING SYSTEMS

In theory the output is a perfect square wave but in practice it depends on the characteristics of the individual gates, and dedicated astable ICs or 555 timer ICs should be used wherever possible.

In summary the NOT gate astable has:

mark-time	$t_1 = 1.1CR$
space-time	$t_2 = 1.1CR$
astable period	$T \approx 2CR$
astable frequency	$f \approx \dfrac{1}{2CR}$

Non-polarised capacitors should be used for C.

Logic gate astable circuits are not very suitable for producing low-frequency pulses because polarised (high-capacitance) capacitors cannot be used.

A **cathode ray oscilloscope** (CRO) can be connected across the output to observe the waveform of a high-frequency pulse. A typical CRO is shown in Fig 6.10.

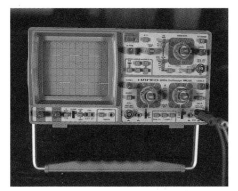

Fig 6.10 Cathode ray oscilloscope (CRO).

Example: The circuit in Fig 6.8 is constructed with $R = 100\,k\Omega$, $C = 0.047\,\mu F$. The CRO is connected across the output and the display obtained is shown in Fig 6.11. The **time base** setting is at **2 ms/div** (2 millisecond per division of the grid) and the **Volts/div** setting is at **1 V/div**. Use the grid to calculate **(a)** the astable period and **(b)** the amplitude of the pulse. **(c)** What is the frequency of the pulse?

(a) Period $= 2\,\text{ms/div} \times 5\,\text{divisions} = 10\,\text{ms}$
(b) Amplitude $= 1\,\text{V/div} \times 5\,\text{divisions} = 5\,\text{V}$

(c) Frequency $= \dfrac{1}{10 \times 10^{-3}\,\text{s}} = 100\,\text{Hz}$

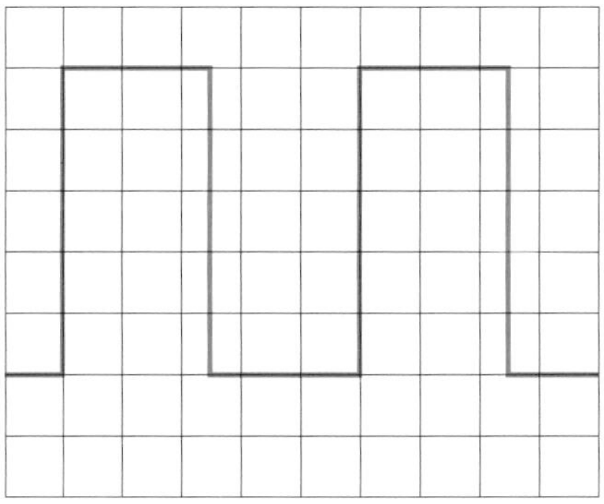

Fig 6.11 CRO display obtained in the example.

6.4 THE 555 TIMER IC

The **555 timer IC** is an integrated circuit which can be made to function as a **monostable** or **astable** circuit with the external addition of **resistors and capacitors**. The pin diagram is shown in Fig 6.12. There are two main types of 555 available: the bipolar and the CMOS version. The advantage of using these ICs over logic ICs to construct timing circuits is their high output current (200 mA for bipolar, 100 mA for CMOS), allowing relatively large loads to be driven directly, and also their ability to produce accurate and repeatable time periods.

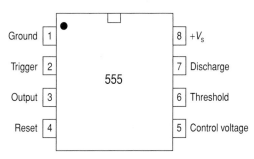

Fig 6.12 Pin diagram for the 555 timer IC.

Both ICs operate from a wide voltage range (4.5–15 V for bipolar, 2–15 V for CMOS). The advantage of the CMOS over the bipolar 555 is that it requires less current to operate it (120 µA compared with the bipolar's 10 mA), which makes it a useful device for battery-operated equipment. The investigations in this book assume the use of the lower-cost bipolar type.

The 555 monostable

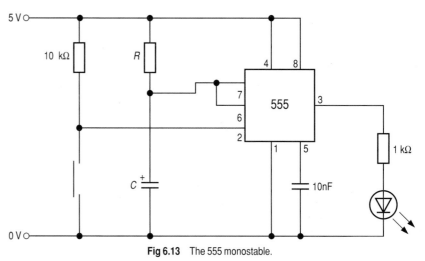

Fig 6.13　The 555 monostable.

To construct a monostable, a resistor and capacitor are added to the IC as in Fig 6.13. When the device is triggered (pin 2) on a falling edge (logic 1 to logic 0), the output (pin 3) goes high for a time given by the equation:

monostable period　　$T = 1.1\,CR$

where C is in farads (F), R in ohms (Ω) and T in seconds (s). It is useful to recognise that if C is in microfarads (μF) and R is in megohms (MΩ), then T is also in seconds.

A data sheet (available from RS, reference J2113) shows the internal circuitry of the 555 IC, and the equation for the monostable period can be derived once a knowledge is gained of the various subsystems within the IC.

Important notes for practical work

For the monostable action to work, the monostable period must be longer than the trigger pulse.

The 10 nF capacitor **coupling** pin 5 with 0 V is needed to prevent the circuit from false triggering.

A 555 timer can produce brief dips of voltage on the supply line. If logic gates are used with 555 timers, a large-value (100 μF) electrolytic capacitor should be connected across the power supply (negative terminal of capacitor to 0 V) to eliminate the voltage change; this is called **decoupling** the supply.

If electrolytic capacitors are used for C, their working voltage should be close to (but more than) the supply voltage (6.3 V electrolytic capacitors are available if the supply voltage is 5 V).

The recommended range of values for R is between 1 kΩ and 1 MΩ, and for C between 10 nF and 10 μF. If electrolytic capacitors are used, their high leakage current and poor tolerance may result in the timing period being a long way from that predicted by the formula.

INVESTIGATION

The 555 monostable

Construct the monostable circuit shown in Fig 6.13 on a breadboard and investigate the effect on the monostable period of varying the capacitor C and resistor R values. Select values that will give a measurable time delay. The value of the LED's series resistor depends on the supply voltage (4.5–15 V d.c.) being used. Compare the actual value for the monostable period with its theoretical value, $T = 1.1CR$.

Once triggered, the 555 output remains high until the end of the monostable period. The basic circuit (Fig 6.13) cannot be re-triggered to extend the period.

TIMING SYSTEMS

Re-triggerable monostable ICs are available. The 74HC123 is a dual re-triggerable monostable IC containing two separate monostables which can be used independently.

QUESTIONS

6.1 The 555 monostable circuit in Fig 6.13 is set up with $R = 470\,\text{k}\Omega$ and $C = 22\,\mu\text{F}$. Calculate the monostable period.

6.2 A 555 timer is to be used to produce a pulse of duration $150\,\mu\text{s}$. If a $10\,\text{nF}$ capacitor is to be used, determine a suitable value for the resistor.

555 instrumentation applications
By replacing R_2 in Fig 6.14 with an LDR and by selecting suitable values for R_1 and C such as $1\,\text{k}\Omega$ and $10\,\text{nF}$ respectively, the circuit can be used as a light-to-frequency converter. The frequency of the output pulse will depend on the illumination of the LDR, producing a high-frequency pulse in bright light and a low-frequency pulse in darkness.

The 555 astable

Fig 6.14 shows how a 555 IC can be used in **astable** mode. The trigger (pin 2) is connected to pin 6. Therefore, at the end of the first pulse, the trigger is connected low again, starting another pulse. R_2 is needed to prevent C discharging too quickly, which would make the space-time too short. The formulae for this circuit are given below:

$$\text{mark-time} \qquad t_1 = 0.7(R_1 + R_2)\,C$$

$$\text{space-time} \qquad t_2 = 0.7R_2C$$

$$\text{astable period} \qquad T = t_1 + t_2$$

$$\text{astable frequency} \qquad f = \frac{1}{t_1 + t_2}$$

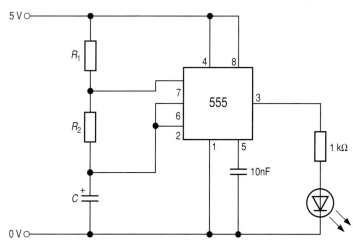

Fig 6.14   The 555 astable.

This basic circuit will not allow a mark-to-space ratio of 1:1 since the mark-time is always greater than the space-time. In theory, an **oscillator with an equal mark-time and space-time** can be constructed by **ignoring the discharge terminal** (pin 7) and connecting a resistor from the output (pin 3) to pin 6 to charge and discharge the capacitor, (see Fig. 6.15). The formulae for the circuit in Fig 6.15 are:

$$\text{mark-time} = \text{space-time} \qquad t = 0.7CR$$

$$\text{astable period} \qquad T = 1.4CR$$

$$\text{astable frequency} \qquad f = \frac{1}{1.4CR}$$

Square wave producer
A more practicable version of the circuit in Fig 6.15 is to make R_2 much larger than R_1 in Fig 6.14. For example if $R_1 = 1\,\text{k}\Omega$ and $R_2 = 1\,\text{k}\Omega$ the output waveform is *almost* a square wave, with a 1:1 mark-to-space ratio.

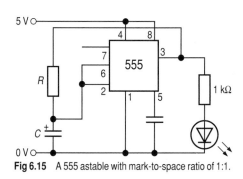

Fig 6.15   A 555 astable with mark-to-space ratio of 1:1.

INVESTIGATION	**The 555 astable**

Construct the 555 astable circuit in Fig 6.14 on a breadboard. Calculate the mark-time, space-time and frequency for different resistor and capacitor values. Use a stop-clock to measure low-frequency and a CRO for high-frequency pulses. Investigate the effect of connecting a loudspeaker (read the section below first) to the output for high audio-frequency pulses (i.e. audible to the human ear – 20 Hz to 20 kHz).

Audio oscillator

The coil of a **loudspeaker** (Fig 6.16(a)) can be made to vibrate if there is an **alternating current** (a.c.) through the coil. If the digital output pulses from an astable are used to vibrate the coil, the current does not reverse direction, but simply switches on and off. This on/off action can set up a mean direct current (d.c.) through the coil which must be eliminated for the loudspeaker to function correctly. Therefore, the output from the 555 astable should be coupled to the loudspeaker through an electrolytic capacitor as in Fig 6.16(b) because the capacitor **blocks** any flow of direct current but still allows a signal to pass.

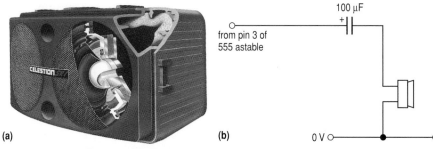

(a)   **(b)**

Fig 6.16 **(a)** A typical loudspeaker. **(b)** A loudspeaker with coupling capacitor.

QUESTIONS	

6.3 A 555 timer operating in astable mode has a frequency of 5 kHz using a capacitor of 10 nF. Determine the required values of R_1 and R_2 assuming they are equal.

6.4 Using the values of R_1 and R_2 calculated in question 6.3, determine the value of C required to adjust the frequency to 50 Hz.

SUMMARY

A monostable produces a single pulse for a time determined by an RC network.

Logic gate monostable period $= 0.7CR$
555 monostable period $= 1.1CR$

An astable produces a continuous pulse; the frequency is determined by an RC network.

Astable period = mark-time + space-time, $T = t_1 + t_2$

Frequency, $f = \dfrac{1}{T}$

Logic gate astable period, $T \approx 2CR$
555 astable: $t_1 = 0.7(R_1 + R_2)C$, $t_2 = 0.7R_2C$, $T = t_1 + t_2$

Chapter 7

COUNTING SYSTEMS

LEARNING OBJECTIVES

After studying this chapter you should be able to:

1. construct a bistable latch from NAND and NOR gates;

2. explain the action of D-type and J–K flip-flops;

3. understand the use of Schmitt triggers and debouncing circuits for pulse shaping;

4. understand what is meant by the modulo of a counter;

5. explain the operation of asynchronous and synchronous counters;

6. state the advantages of quartz oscillators compared to free-running astables;

7. understand the principle of the digital clock.

7.1 SEQUENTIAL LOGIC SYSTEMS

In combinational logic systems (Chapter 5) the output state at any instant is determined by the input state at that time. In **sequential** logic systems the output state is a function not only of the current input state but also of the previous inputs that led to the current state. In order to construct a sequential system a circuit is needed that is capable of storing a logic signal (that is, it must have a **memory**). **Bistable** circuits exhibit this property. There are several types of bistable circuit, but unfortunately no general agreement on which names should be used for these classes of device. The terminology adopted here refers to a level-sensitive device as a **latch** and an edge-triggered device as a **flip-flop**.

Flip-flops are the basic building blocks of **counters**, **frequency dividers**, **shift registers** and **memories**. Counters and dividers will be considered in this chapter; registers and memories will be looked at in Chapter 11.

Multivibrators
There are three types of multivibrator systems: astable, monostable and bistable.

Clock pulses

Sequential logic circuits are divided into **synchronous** and **asynchronous** systems. In synchronous systems the output does not respond immediately to an input change but waits until it receives a **clock pulse**. In asynchronous systems, successive stages are triggered by the completion of the operation of the preceding stage.

A 'clock' in digital electronics is referred to as a **pulse generator** if it is provided by an astable or a monostable circuit. An astable is a continuous-pulse producer and a monostable is a single-pulse producer. There are two main types of clock triggering, **level** and **edge**. In level-triggered sequential systems, changes occur at the output of the system when the level of the clock pulse is at logic 1 or at logic 0. In edge triggering, changes occur either during the rise of a clock pulse from logic 0 to logic 1 (**rising** or **positive-edge**

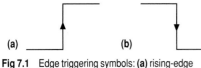

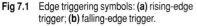

Fig 7.1 Edge triggering symbols: **(a)** rising-edge trigger; **(b)** falling-edge trigger.

triggering) or during the fall from logic 1 to logic 0 (**falling** or **negative-edge** triggering). The symbols used to represent edge triggering are shown in Fig 7.1.

Clock pulses can be supplied by an astable or **crystal oscillator** or by a **debounced** mechanical switch. The clock pulses fed into a counter must be clean, i.e. **free from noise, with rapid rise and fall times**. A **Schmitt trigger** circuit can be used for **pulse shaping** to produce clean sharp pulses and for switch debouncing. The output of a Schmitt trigger switches on and off at two specific input voltages called the upper and lower threshold voltages or the **upper** and **lower trigger points** (**UTP** and **LTP**). The 74HC132 NAND Schmitt trigger has a UTP of 2.7 V and a LTP of 1.5 V. This means that **if the input voltage rises, the output will rapidly change state from logic 1 to logic 0** when the input voltage is 2.7 V. **The output will remain in this low state until the input voltage falls** to 1.5 V **when the output will rapidly rise to logic 1**. This difference between these two voltage trigger points (1.2 V) is called the **hysteresis** or backlash, and it is this property of the Schmitt trigger which prevents the output triggering on and off when the input is wavering on the borderline switching voltage. Fig 7.2 shows how a Schmitt trigger is used to convert a slowly changing input voltage into the sharp on/off signal used in digital systems. Fig 7.3 shows how it cleans up a noisy input signal.

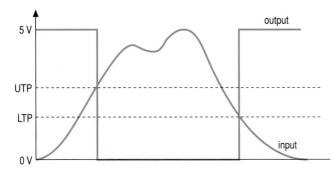

Fig 7.2 Sharpening a slowly changing signal using a Schmitt trigger.

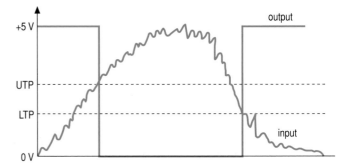

Fig 7.3 Cleaning up a noisy signal using a Schmitt trigger.

Switch debouncing

If mechanical switches are used to provide clock pulses, their contact '**bounce**' must be eliminated, otherwise unwanted pulses might occur if the contacts bounce back and forth rapidly when the switch is closed. One way of achieving **debouncing** is to use a Schmitt trigger as in Fig 7.4. Contact bounce is prevented due to the discharging action of the capacitor.

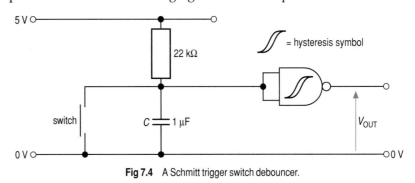

Fig 7.4 A Schmitt trigger switch debouncer.

7.2 BISTABLES

A bistable has **two stable states**. One output state stays high and the other low (the outputs are **complementary**) until an external input signal switches the high state to low and the low state to high. There are several different types of bistable: S–R type, D type, T type and J–K type.

COUNTING SYSTEMS

S–R latch

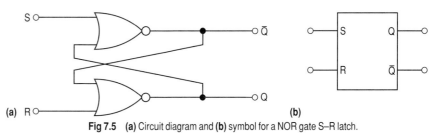

Fig 7.5 **(a)** Circuit diagram and **(b)** symbol for a NOR gate S–R latch.

An S–R latch can be constructed from two NOR gates. Fig 7.5 shows the circuit diagram and symbol for an S–R latch. It has two inputs, the **set S** and **reset R**, and two output states, **Q** and $\overline{\text{Q}}$. $\overline{\text{Q}}$ is the complementary state to Q. The truth table or **transition table,** since some states depend on what happened in the previous state, is shown in Table 7.1.

Transition tables
The arrow ($\rightarrow$) in the transition tables indicates that a change in the input results in the output data being stored or reset to 0.

Table 7.1   Transition table for NOR bistable

S	R	Q	$\overline{\text{Q}}$	
1	0	1	0	$S = 1$ sets $\overline{\text{Q}} = 0$ and $Q = 1$ (SET)
$\rightarrow$0	0	1	0	The outputs remain in their previous states
0	$\rightarrow$1	0	1	$R = 1$ sets $\overline{\text{Q}} = 1$ and $Q = 0$ (RESET)
0	$\rightarrow$0	0	1	The outputs remain in their previous states
1	1	0	0	Indeterminate state (not allowed)

With reset R low, when S goes high, Q goes high. With R still low, when S goes low, Q remains high until R goes high. The opposite happens at $\overline{\text{Q}}$. It should be noted that the condition $S = R = 1$ results in both outputs being 0. The two outputs are no longer the inverse of each other and the circuit no longer functions as a bistable. Therefore this combination of inputs is generally forbidden. S–R bistables are called **latch** circuits since the output remains high, i.e. latched on, when the input changes state and remains on until a reset signal is received.

Fig 7.6 illustrates the input and output waveforms of the S–R latch. The diagrams assume that the latch responds immediately to changes at the input. In practice there is a slight delay called the propagation delay, which is 8 ns for the 74HC02. When gates are connected together, this delay can cause unwanted pulses or **glitches** in the circuit.

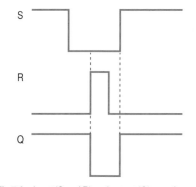

Fig 7.6   Input (S and R) and output (Q) waveforms for an S–R latch.

$\overline{\text{S}}$–$\overline{\text{R}}$ latch

An $\overline{\text{S}}$–$\overline{\text{R}}$ latch can be constructed from two NAND gates. Fig 7.7 shows the circuit diagram and symbol for an $\overline{\text{S}}$–$\overline{\text{R}}$ latch. The transition table is shown in Table 7.2.

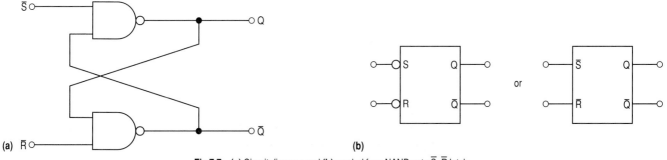

Fig 7.7 **(a)** Circuit diagram and **(b)** symbol for a NAND gate $\overline{\text{S}}$–$\overline{\text{R}}$ latch.

Table 7.2   Transition table for NAND bistable

$\overline{S}$	$\overline{R}$	Q	$\overline{Q}$	
0	1	1	0	$\overline{S} = 0$ sets Q = 1 (SET)
→1	1	1	0	The outputs remain in their previous states
1	→0	0	1	$\overline{R} = 0$ sets $\overline{Q} = 1$ and Q = 0 (RESET)
1	→1	0	1	The outputs remain in their previous states
0	0	0	0	Indeterminate state (not allowed)

Comparing the output of the NAND gate bistable with that of the NOR gate version, it can be seen that, for the NOR gate circuit, taking S *high* sets Q = 1 and taking R *high* resets Q to 0. S and R are therefore referred to as **active high** inputs. For the NAND gate circuit, the set input must be taken *low* to set Q = 1 and the reset input must also be taken *low* to reset Q to 0. $\overline{S}$ and $\overline{R}$ are now referred to as **active low** inputs; hence the use of the inverted symbols.

INVESTIGATION

The S–R and $\overline{S}$–$\overline{R}$ latches

Basic apparatus: 74HC02 (quad two-input NOR IC); 74HC00 (quad two-input NAND IC); 100 kΩ resistors; low-current LEDs; series resistors; breadboard; push switches.

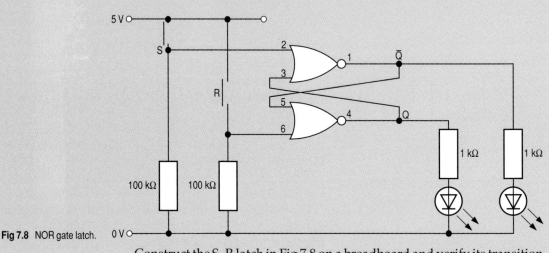

Fig 7.8 NOR gate latch.

Construct the S–R latch in Fig 7.8 on a breadboard and verify its transition table (Table 7.1). Repeat this for the $\overline{S}$–$\overline{R}$ latch using a similar circuit and verify Table 7.2.

Another means of debouncing a switch is to use an $\overline{S}$–$\overline{R}$ latch as in Fig 7.9.

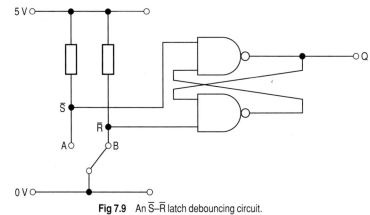

Fig 7.9 An $\overline{S}$–$\overline{R}$ latch debouncing circuit.

QUESTION

7.1 To understand how the debouncing circuit (Fig 7.9) operates, copy and complete Table 7.3 to show the logic levels when the switch moves from B to A. On reaching A, the switch bounces from A (it does not bounce back as far as B) before settling at A.

Table 7.3   Results for question 7.1

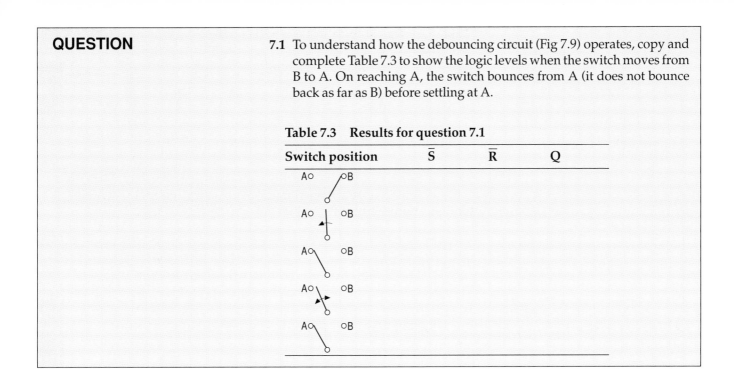

Switch position	$\bar{S}$	$\bar{R}$	Q

D-type latch

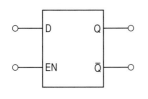

Fig 7.10   D-type latch.

Another form of latch is the D-type latch (Fig 7.10). The **enable** (EN) or clock input can be used to allow (enable) or inhibit (disable) the action of the D (**data**) input. If the enable is high, the D input determines the output state. If D is high, the latch will be set with Q = 1. If D is low, the output will be reset with Q = 0. When the enable input signal is low, the latch is placed in its **memory mode** preventing any change of state. The output remembers the value of D when the enable went low. Fig 7.11 illustrates the input and output waveforms for a D-type latch.

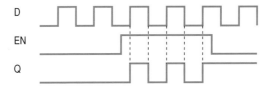

Fig 7.11   Input (D and EN) and output (Q) waveforms for a D-type latch.

The D-type latch suffers from one defect, i.e. it is **transparent**. When enable is high, the output Q changes in response to the input data at D. **Edge-triggered** bistables or flip-flops and **master–slave** flip-flops are not transparent. The outputs of these devices can only change state at the instant that a trigger pulse is received (flip-flops may be positive- or negative-edge triggered).

D-type flip-flop

Edge notation
The triangle used on the clock input of Fig 7.12 represents an edge-triggered device.

The D-type flip-flop is a clocked S–R bistable operated from just one input. The NOR and NAND gate bistables both had an indeterminate state (S = R = 1). The D-type flip-flop overcomes this problem because it only has one data input. The symbols for D-type flip-flops are shown in Fig 7.12. The transition table for a positive-edge triggered D-type flip-flop is shown in Table 7.4.

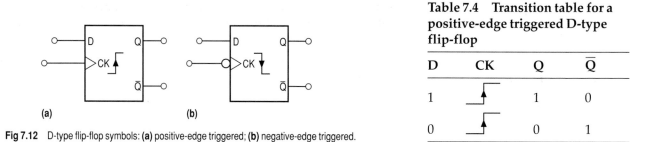

(a)　　　　　**(b)**

Fig 7.12　D-type flip-flop symbols: **(a)** positive-edge triggered; **(b)** negative-edge triggered.

Table 7.4　Transition table for a positive-edge triggered D-type flip-flop

D	CK	Q	$\overline{Q}$
1	⌐	1	0
0	⌐	0	1

The output Q of the D-type flip-flop assumes the state of the D input when a rising-edge clock pulse is received.

J–K flip-flop

The J–K flip-flop (Fig 7.13) is similar to the S–R bistable with two inputs (J and K) but the indeterminate state is no longer prohibited. The transition table for a negative-edge triggered J–K flip-flop is shown in Table 7.5.

Table 7.5　Transition table for a negative-edge triggered J–K flip-flop

J	K	CK	Q	$\overline{Q}$
0	0	⌐_	No change	
0	1	⌐_	0	1
1	0	⌐_	1	0
1	1	⌐_	Toggle	

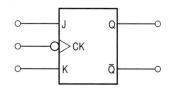

Fig 7.13　J–K flip-flop.

If both J and K are low, the negative edge of the clock pulse causes no change to the outputs. If J is low and K is high, the next clock pulse takes Q low and $\overline{Q}$ high. If J is high and K is low, the clock pulse takes Q high and $\overline{Q}$ low. If J and K are both high, each negative edge of the clock pulse changes the state of both outputs, i.e. the output **toggles** on and off. **When J = K = 1, the flip-flop is operating as a toggle or T-type flip-flop.** The symbol for a T-type flip-flop is shown in Fig 7.14 and Fig 7.15 illustrates the operation of this type of flip-flop.

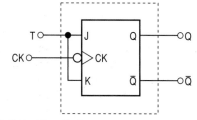

Fig 7.14　T-type flip-flop.

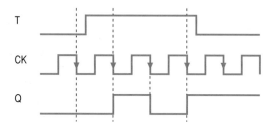

Fig 7.15　Input (T), clock (CK) and output (Q) waveforms for a T-type latch.

Reset operation

The control inputs (e.g. J, K and D) of the edge-triggered bistables considered here are referred to as synchronous because they only affect the output when a suitable trigger input is received. In many applications it is necessary to be able to reset the outputs independent of the clock, so flip-flops have additional inputs to perform this operation. These additional inputs are called

asynchronous inputs because they are independent of the clock. Unfortunately manufacturers are unable to agree on common names for these inputs – the terms **preset**, **clear** and **reset** are commonly used.

INVESTIGATION

The J–K flip-flop

Basic apparatus: 74HC73 (dual J–K flip-flop); signal generator; debounced switch; low-current LEDs.

Construct the circuit in Fig 7.16 on a breadboard and check the validity of the transition table in Table 7.5. The reset pin 6 should normally be high. Connect pin 6 to 0 V to reset the flip-flop.

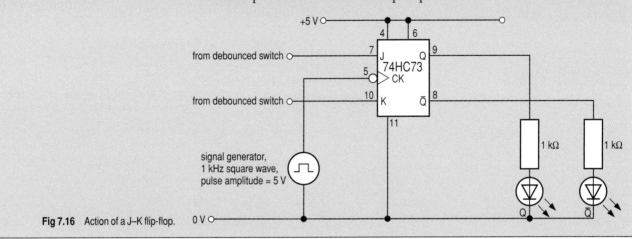

Fig 7.16   Action of a J–K flip-flop.

Master–slave flip-flops

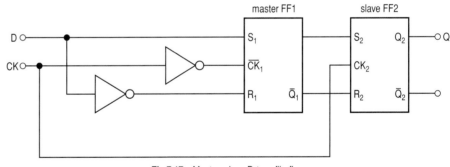

Master–slave notation
Master–slave flip-flops are usually labelled M/S to distinguish them from other types.

Fig 7.17   Master–slave D-type flip-flop.

The D-type latch is transparent. One way of preventing a bistable circuit from being transparent when the enable or clock input is at logic 1 is to use a master–slave flip-flop. The D-type master–slave flip-flop in Fig 7.17 consists of two S–R flip-flops with their clock inputs coupled via an inverter. (A clocked S–R bistable can only change its output state when the clock input is held high. When the clock input is low, the output stays in its previous state.) The outputs of the master flip-flop, FF1, are connected to the S and R inputs of the slave, FF2. The input and output waveforms of the master–slave circuit are illustrated in Fig 7.18. For the master FF1, when CK is low, $\overline{CK_1}$ is high, and the output Q_1 follows its data input D, i.e. the master flip-flop is transparent. When CK is high, the output of the master maintains its previous outputs. However, when CK is high, the clock to the slave flip-flop is high, the output Q_2 follows its input at S_2 and the slave is now transparent. When CK is low, the output of the slave maintains its previous outputs. In a master–slave flip-flop, only one of the two flip-flops is transparent at any one instant. The result of this is that the output of the master–slave, Q, takes the value of the input D at the instant that the clock pulse rises from low to high.

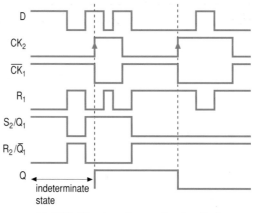

Fig 7.18 Waveforms for a master–slave flip-flop.

7.3 COUNTERS

A simple two-bit **binary counter** can be constructed from two D-type flip-flops as in Fig 7.19 where the D input is fed to $\overline{Q}$ of each flip-flop.

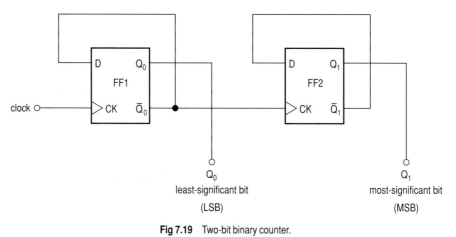

Fig 7.19 Two-bit binary counter.

Recall:
- The output Q becomes the same as the state of the D input when a clock pulse is received.

- $\overline{Q}$ is in the opposite state to Q.

Assume:
- The D-type flip-flops are positive-edge triggered.
- The Q outputs from both flip-flops are initially held low before a clock pulse is received.

The transition table in Table 7.6 explains the function of this circuit.

Table 7.6   Transition table for the two-bit counter

'x' in Table 7.6 = no clock pulse

FF1				FF2			
CK	D	Q (Q_0)	$\overline{Q}$	CK	D	Q (Q_1)	$\overline{Q}$
x	1	0	1	x	1	0	1
⌐↑	0	1	0	0	1	0	1
⌐↑	1	0	1	⌐↑	0	1	0
⌐↑	0	1	0	⌐↓	0	1	0

COUNTING SYSTEMS

Two-bit binary counter

Basic apparatus: 2 × 74HC74 (dual D-type flip-flop); debounced switch; low-current LEDs

Construct the two-bit counter in Fig 7.20 on a breadboard. For normal operation, the preset and reset inputs should be connected to +5 V. Each flip-flop can be reset (Q = 0) by taking the reset pin low and keeping preset high. Reset must be returned high for the circuit to count.

Use another 74HC74 to construct a four-bit binary counter.

Pin connections:

Pin number	
4	preset FF1
1	reset FF1
10	preset FF2
13	reset FF2
14	+5 V
7	0 V

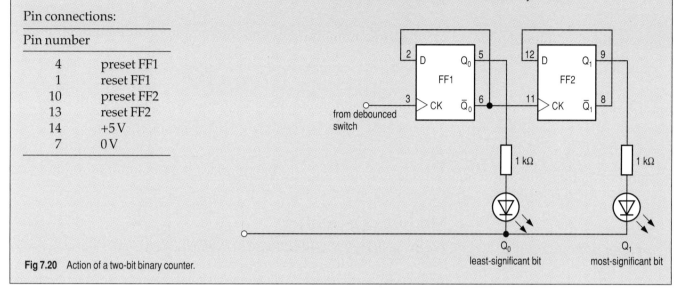

Fig 7.20   Action of a two-bit binary counter.

Asynchronous counters

When counters are constructed by connecting flip-flops in series as in Fig 7.21, they are referred to as '**ripple through**' or **asynchronous counters**.

The circuit in Fig 7.21 consists of four negative-edge triggered J–K flip-flops arranged to toggle by connecting the J and K inputs to logic 1. The output of each flip-flop provides the clock input of the next flip-flop. When a square wave clock signal of frequency f is applied to the binary counter, the output of the first flip-flop, Q_0, toggles on each falling edge of the clock pulse, producing a square waveform at half the clock frequency. Q_1 toggles on each falling edge Q_0 and therefore produces a square waveform at half the frequency of Q_0 or at one-quarter of the clock frequency. Each successive stage divides the clock frequency by a factor of 2 and so the counter can be thought of as a **frequency divider.**

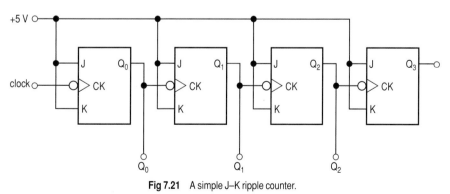

Fig 7.21   A simple J–K ripple counter.

Table 7.7 shows the sequence of '1's and '0's which appear on the outputs of the flip-flops after each clock pulse. The pattern of the outputs represents the binary code for the number of pulses applied to the circuit. The arrangement therefore represents a counter.

Table 7.7 Output sequence for a four-bit counter

Number of clock pulses	Q_3	Q_2	Q_1	Q_0
0	0	0	0	0
1	0	0	0	1
2	0	0	1	0
3	0	0	1	1
4	0	1	0	0
5	0	1	0	1
6	0	1	1	0
7	0	1	1	1
8	1	0	0	0
9	1	0	0	1
10	1	0	1	0
11	1	0	1	1
12	1	1	0	0
13	1	1	0	1
14	1	1	1	0
15	1	1	1	1

Modulo of a counter

The circuit in Fig 7.21 counts from 0 to 15 (binary 0000 to 1111) and then resets to zero. The **modulo** of a counter refers to the number of output states it goes through before resetting to zero. A four-bit binary counter uses four flip-flops and can produce a four-bit binary pattern, i.e. it has 16 (2^4 where 4 is the number of flip-flops) output states representing a modulo-16 counter.

QUESTION

7.2 What is the modulo of an eight-bit binary counter?

A counter with n flip-flops can be reset before 2^n states using an AND gate. Fig 7.22 shows a modulo-10 counter.

When the binary word is 1010 after 10 clock pulses, Q_1 and Q_3 are at logic 1; therefore the output of the AND gate is at logic 1, which resets the counter instantly to 0000. This is known as a **binary-coded decimal** (BCD) counter.

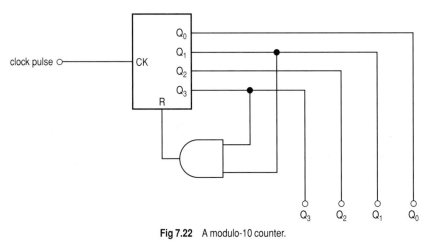

Fig 7.22 A modulo-10 counter.

Propagation delay in ripple counters

In a ripple counter the effects of the input are propagated along the series of flip-flops, each circuit adding its own delay. If each flip-flop in the asynchronous counter has a propagation delay of 18 ns and four of them are

COUNTING SYSTEMS

connected together, the total time delay for the pulse to 'ripple through' is 72 ns, which means that the **maximum clock pulse rate** (maximum clock frequency) will be limited to:

$$\frac{1}{72 \times 10^{-9}} = 14 \times 10^6 \text{ Hz} = 14 \text{ MHz}$$

If clock pulses are received by the first flip-flop before the last one has responded, the counter will not, at any time, read the correct value.

Synchronous counters

Synchronous counters overcome this problem since the clock of each flip-flop is connected to the input clock pulse, so each flip-flop is toggled simultaneously, therefore increasing the speed of operation. Fig 7.23 shows a synchronous four-bit counter constructed from four negative-edge triggered J–K flip-flops. The outputs are connected to an AND gate at each stage. Q_0 changes on the negative edge of each clock pulse. Q_1 changes state on the negative edge of a clock pulse when Q_0 is high. Q_2 changes state on the negative edge of a clock pulse when both Q_0 and Q_1 are high. Q_3 changes state on the negative edge of a clock pulse when Q_0, Q_1 and Q_2 are high.

Fig 7.23 Synchronous counter.

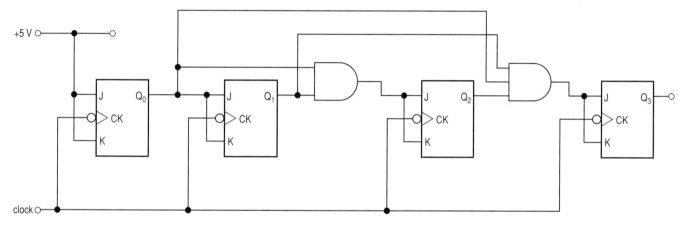

7.4 CRYSTAL OSCILLATORS

The square wave astable circuits considered in Chapter 6 do not have very stable output frequencies. When a stable and precise frequency is required, for example, in digital watches, **crystal-controlled oscillators** are used. Quartz crystals can be cut to oscillate accurately at very high frequencies. The standard crystal used in digital watches oscillates at 32 768 Hz (2^{15} Hz). A 14-bit counter (74HC4060) can be used to divide the frequency by 2^{14} to give an output frequency of 2 Hz. Fig 7.24 shows how a crystal can be connected to a 14-bit binary counter to produce an accurate output frequency of 2 Hz. Limitations of using crystal oscillators arise due to the tolerance of low-cost crystals, which can lead to a significant error in timing if used for very precise measurement.

Fig 7.24 Using a 14-bit counter and a crystal oscillator to obtain a frequency output of 2 Hz.

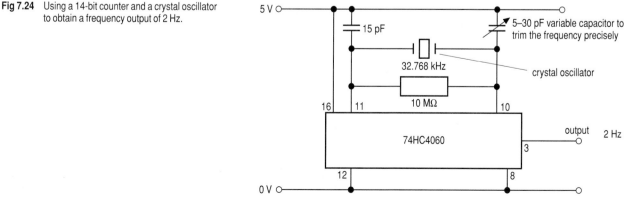

7.5 THE DIGITAL CLOCK

Fig 7.25 shows the block diagram for a digital clock. The knowledge of the process blocks you have gained so far should enable you to understand the operation of the clock.

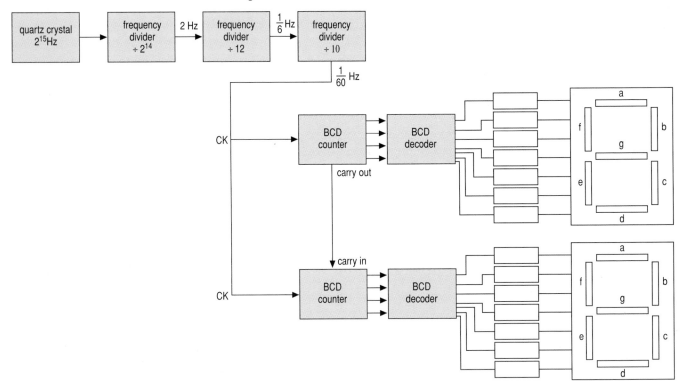

Fig 7.25 Block diagram of the minutes display of a digital clock.

SUMMARY

A bistable has two stable states which change state when triggered.

An S–R bistable can be used as a latch. The output is held high until a reset signal is received. $\overline{S}$–$\overline{R}$ latches are used in debouncing circuits.

The output of a D-type flip-flop changes to the same state as its input when it receives a clock pulse.

A J–K flip-flop retains its present output state if J = K = 0. If J and K are different, it acts like a D-type flip-flop; and if J = K = 1, the output toggles on and off with each clock pulse received.

The clock pulse which triggers a flip-flop should be clean and 'square', but in practice, pulses may be noisy or distorted. A Schmitt trigger is used to clean up a pulse.

Counters use flip-flops. Each flip-flop represents one bit.

The modulo of a counter is the number of output states it goes through before resetting. The reset of a counter can be used with logic gates to make a counter count to any number.

Counters can be used to divide the frequency of a square wave clock pulse.

Theme **3**

ANALOGUE SYSTEMS

Electronic systems are designed to process voltage signals; they cannot process temperature or sound or any other physical quantity. In order to process these real-world quantities, a voltage signal that represents or is a copy of the real-world signal is made. The varying voltage signals produced are called *analogue signals*. Chapter 8 looks at simple audio and radio communication systems which process analogue signals and considers the importance of the amplifier within an analogue system. The use of the operational amplifier in analogue systems is dealt with in Chapter 9.

The Syncom 4 communications satellite was launched from the Space Shuttle 'Discovery'. Modern communications satellites receive, amplify and re-transmit information back to Earth, providing television, telefax, telephone, radio and digital data links around the world. Syncom 4 follows a geosynchronous orbit (also called a geostationary orbit)—that is, it orbits at the same speed as the Earth spins, keeping the satellite in a fixed position above the Earth. This type of orbit enables uninterrupted communication links between ground stations.

Chapter 8

AUDIO AND RADIO SYSTEMS

LEARNING OBJECTIVES

After studying this chapter you should be able to:

1. describe the characteristics and usage of microphones and loudspeakers;

2. understand the use of *RC* and crossover network filters;

3. describe ways of matching the input and output impedances of an amplifier to obtain maximum voltage transfer;

4. understand the push–pull principle used in power amplifiers;

5. describe the function of the subsystems of an AM radio receiver.

8.1 AUDIO SYSTEMS

Audio systems process analogue signals which carry information by means of the shape of their waveform. A requirement of most amplifiers is that the output signal should be an exact copy of the input signal, albeit increased in amplitude. However, the problem with transmitting an analogue signal is that any interference that is picked up will change the shape of the waveform and hence alter the information being received. To overcome this, many audio systems now convert the analogue audio signals into digital and then back again to analogue. This is because a very large amount of interference is needed if a logic 0 is to be misinterpreted as a logic 1.

The simplest type of audio system is the one-way intercom shown in Fig 8.1 where sound waves are picked up by a microphone which generates small varying audio-frequency (a.f.) signals, which are amplified and then converted back into sound waves by a loudspeaker.

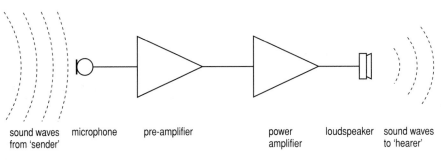

sound waves from 'sender' microphone pre-amplifier power amplifier loudspeaker sound waves to 'hearer'

Fig 8.1 Block diagram of a basic audio system.

The alternating voltage generated by the microphone is typically of the order of millivolts whereas the voltage needed to drive the loudspeaker may be several volts; therefore the need for amplification is obvious. This chapter looks at the fundamental building blocks of a simple audio system and how input and output transducers are interfaced with simple transistor amplifying circuits.

8.2 AUDIO AMPLIFIERS

Audio-frequency (**a.f.**) signals have a range of frequencies (20 Hz to 20 kHz) audible to the human ear. Amplifiers are said to exhibit '**gain**'. The voltage gain of an amplifier is the ratio of its output voltage to input voltage. The general requirement for audio amplifiers is that there is a linear relationship between the input and output voltage, with the output voltage being greater than the input voltage. A linear relationship will ensure that the audio amplifier produces an exact **copy** of the input signal. Similarly, current and power gains are defined as the ratio of the output to the input quantity. Since the power gains of modern electronic amplifiers can be very large, it is convenient to use a logarithmic ratio rather than a linear one. The logarithmic **decibel (dB)** scale, introduced by Alexander Graham Bell as a method of measuring sound levels, compares the strengths of a.f. signals and is a logarithmic ratio between two power levels. The power gain in dB is given by the following equation:

$$\text{power gain (in dB)} = 10\log\left(\frac{P_{\text{OUT}}}{P_{\text{IN}}}\right)$$

where P_{OUT} is the power output and P_{IN} the power input.

QUESTION

8.1 Calculate the gain in dB if the power output from an amplifier increases from 100 mW to 200 mW.

Decibel voltage gain?

It is very common to describe the **voltage gain** of a circuit **in dB** as

$$= 20\log\left(\frac{V_{\text{OUT}}}{V_{\text{IN}}}\right)$$

even when R_1 and R_2 are not equal. However, it is not technically correct to talk about the voltage gain of an amplifier in dB. A circuit with a 'voltage gain of 10 dB' actually means that the circuit has a voltage gain which corresponds to a power gain of 10 dB.

The voltage gain of an amplifier is related to the power gain (in dB) by the following derivation:

$$P_{\text{IN}} = \frac{V_{\text{IN}}^2}{R_{\text{IN}}} \quad \text{and} \quad P_{\text{OUT}} = \frac{V_{\text{OUT}}^2}{R_{\text{OUT}}}$$

If $R_{\text{IN}} = R_{\text{OUT}}$ then

$$\frac{P_{\text{OUT}}}{P_{\text{IN}}} = \frac{V_{\text{OUT}}^2}{V_{\text{IN}}^2}$$

where R_{IN} and R_{OUT} are the input and output resistances of the amplifier. So

$$\text{power gain (in dB)} = 10\log\left(\frac{V_{\text{OUT}}}{V_{\text{IN}}}\right)^2 = 20\log\left(\frac{V_{\text{OUT}}}{V_{\text{IN}}}\right)$$

QUESTION

8.2 Convert the following power gains into voltage gains: **(a)** 80 dB, **(b)** 93 dB, **(c)** 106 dB, **(d)** 60 dB, **(e)** 40 dB.

Decibels can be used to represent both amplification and attenuation (reduction in signal). Amplification will give a positive decibel value and attenuation a negative value. An amplifier with a power gain of 0 dB means that the output power is the same as the input power. Power gains of +3 dB and −3 dB represent a doubling and halving of the power respectively.

QUESTION

8.3 Show that a 50% reduction in **power** represents a loss of 3 dB.

Bandwidth

The frequency response of an amplifier is a measure of its ability to amplify signals over a range of frequencies. Most audio amplifiers are designed to amplify a.f. signals within a specified frequency range by a constant amount. For an *ideal* audio amplifier, the power gain would remain at a constant maximum value over a range of values from 20 Hz to 20 kHz (the audio-frequency range). The frequency response for a *typical* audio amplifier is shown in Fig 8.2. (Note that the horizontal frequency scale is logarithmic so that the range of audio frequencies can be represented.) The power gain remains fairly constant over a wide range of audio frequencies but falls at the extreme ends of the range. The reason for this will be explained later.

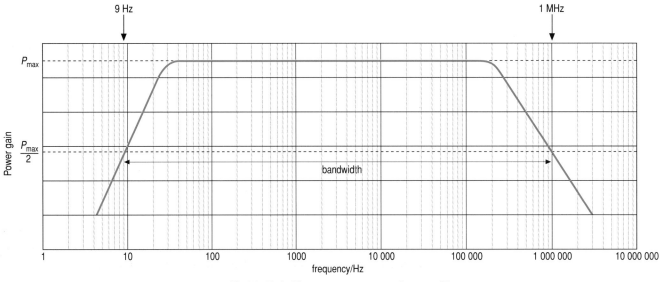

Fig 8.2 Typical frequency response curve for an amplifier.

The **bandwidth** of the amplifier is defined as the frequency range over which the power gain is greater than or equal to half of the maximum gain, or as the frequency range over which the gain does not fall by more than 3 dB from its mid-band value. This is referred to as the **'−3 dB' point**. In terms of voltage gain, the bandwidth is the frequency range over which the voltage gain does not fall below $1/\sqrt{2}$ (i.e. 0.7) of its maximum value, since if the amplifier has equal input and output resistances, the voltage gain is proportional to the square root of the power gain.

Our simple audio system in Fig 8.1 contains an amplifier with two stages: a pre-amplifier to amplify the small signals generated by the microphone and a power amplifier necessary to drive the loudspeaker. Amplifiers can be constructed from transistors.

IC amplifiers
Advances in electronics have largely rendered the discrete transistor amplifier obsolete and it is now more cost effective to make use of linear amplifier ICs.

8.3 BIPOLAR TRANSISTOR PRE-AMPLIFIERS

Common-emitter small-signal amplifiers

The simplest form of **small-signal amplifier** uses a bipolar transistor in common-emitter mode as shown in Fig 8.3. In order to operate in a linear mode so that the output signal is a replica of the input signal, it is necessary to bias the transistor so that it is operating in its linear region (Fig 8.4). This is achieved using the potential divider bias network, R_1 and R_2. There are basically three distinct parts to this circuit: the inverter circuit, the potential divider bias network and the coupling capacitors, C_1 and C_2.

AUDIO AND RADIO SYSTEMS

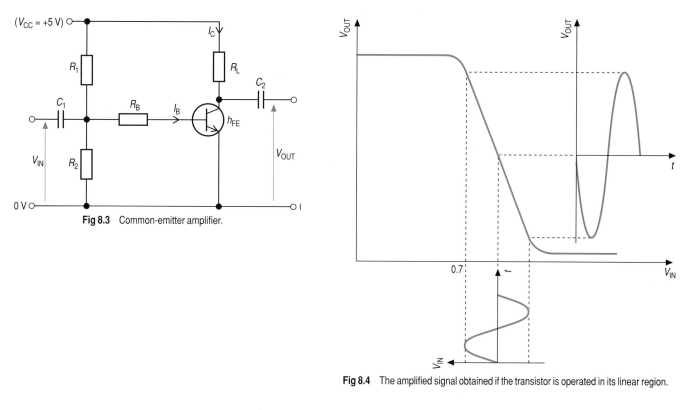

Fig 8.3 Common-emitter amplifier.

Fig 8.4 The amplified signal obtained if the transistor is operated in its linear region.

The inverter

The inverter part of the amplifier circuit is redrawn in Fig 8.5 and the graph in Fig 8.6 shows what happens to the output voltage when the input voltage is increased. The inverter characteristics are obvious from the graph.

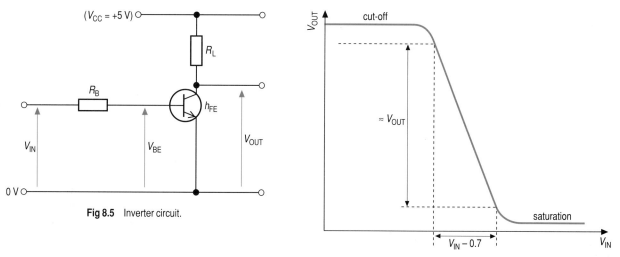

Fig 8.5 Inverter circuit.

Fig 8.6 Variation of output voltage with input voltage for the inverter.

When V_{IN} is below 0.7 V the transistor is switched off. There is no collector current so there is no p.d. across the load resistor R_L; therefore $V_{OUT} = 5$ V. When V_{IN} is greater than 0.7 V, the transistor switches on. There is now a collector current causing the p.d. across R_L to increase. The p.d. across the base and emitter, V_{BE}, cannot rise above 0.7 V so any increase in V_{IN} will provide a greater p.d. across the base resistor R_B causing a larger base current. This increase in the base current will cause the collector current to increase, causing a further increase in the p.d. across R_L. As the p.d. across R_L increases, V_{OUT} decreases. The transistor saturates when $V_{OUT} \approx 0.2$ V. At this point, any further increase in the base current will not affect the collector current.

The **alternating current** (a.c.) **gain** is defined as the ratio of the change of output voltage to the change of input voltage, which is the gradient of the linear region of the graph in Fig 8.6. In order to derive an equation for a.c. gain, in terms of component values, the assumption is made that the transistor saturates when $V_{OUT} = 0$ V, so that the change of V_{OUT} will be equal to the p.d. across the load resistor R_L which is approximately the case when $V_{OUT} \approx 0.2$ V. Therefore

$$\text{a.c. gain} = -\frac{\text{p.d. across } R_L \text{ when transistor is saturated}}{\text{p.d. across } R_B}$$

$$= -\frac{I_C R_L}{I_B R_B} = -h_{FE} \frac{R_L}{R_B}$$

Therefore if the transistor is biased so that it lies in its linear region, any change of V_{IN} causes a change of V_{OUT} that is $h_{FE}(R_L/R_B)$ larger and is of the opposite sign. The purpose of the resistors R_1 and R_2 is to bias the transistor. The transistor is biased at the centre of its linear region so that V_{OUT} can swing equal amounts in both directions. Compare the graphs in Fig 8.7 to the one in Fig 8.4. If the bias voltage is too small or too large, the output will be **clipped** (distorted) as in Fig 8.7(a) and Fig 8.7(b).

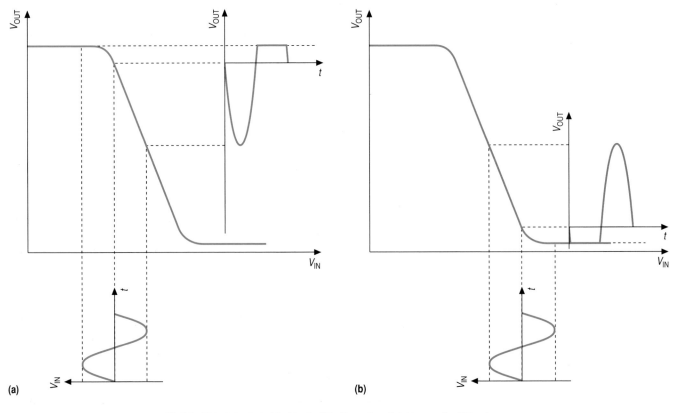

Fig 8.7 Distorted output of the inverter if the bias voltage is **(a)** too small or **(b)** too large.

The bias network

When no input voltage is applied ($V_{IN} = 0$) the transistor is said to be in its **quiescent state**. Component values for R_1 and R_2 are chosen so that the quiescent collector–emitter voltage is about equal to half the supply voltage ($V_{CE} \approx \frac{1}{2} V_{CC}$) so that the transistor is biased at the centre of its linear region. A common-emitter amplifier is set up as in Fig 8.8 using a BC108 transistor, the parameters of which are given in the caption.

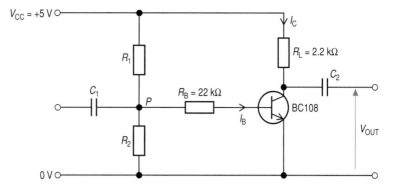

Fig 8.8 Common-emitter amplifier set up using a BC108 transistor. (BC108 parameters: $h_{FE} = 125$ when $I_C = 2$ mA; quiescent state when $V_{CE} \approx \frac{1}{2}V_{CC} = 2.5$ V.)

The following calculation demonstrates how to determine suitable values of R_1 and R_2 so that $V_{CE} \approx \frac{1}{2}V_{CC}$: The p.d. across R_L is $V_{CC} - 2.5$ V = 2.5 V, i.e.

$$I_C R_L = 2.5\,\text{V}$$

$$I_C = \frac{2.5\,\text{V}}{2.2\,\text{k}\Omega} = 1.14\,\text{mA}$$

$$I_B = \frac{I_C}{h_{FE}} = \frac{1.14}{125} = 9.09 \times 10^{-3}\,\text{mA}$$

The p.d. across R_B is $9.09 \times 10^{-3}\,\text{mA} \times 22\,\text{k}\Omega = 0.2$ V. The emitter is connected to 0 V. Therefore the potential at point P is

$$V_P = 0.2 + 0.7 = 0.9\,\text{V}$$

Using the potential divider formula:

$$\frac{R_2}{R_1 + R_2} \times 5 = 0.9$$

$$\frac{R_1 + R_2}{R_2} = 5.56 \qquad (1)$$

In theory, by choosing a value for R_1, R_2 can be calculated. However, if the resistor values are too small, the amplifier will have a low input impedance, which will result in a reduction of the a.c. input signal. If the resistor values are too high, the base current drawn will upset the operation of the potential divider network. The base current was calculated to be $9.09 \times 10^{-3}\,\text{mA}$, and therefore this output current should be no more than one-tenth of the current in the divider network. (See notes about loading a potential divider in the box below.) Therefore there must be at least 10 times this base current in R_1 and R_2, i.e. $9.09 \times 10^{-2}\,\text{mA}$.

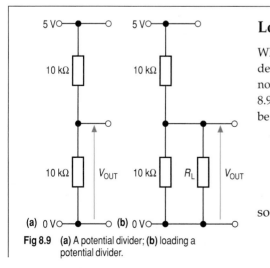

Fig 8.9 **(a)** A potential divider; **(b)** loading a potential divider.

Loading a potential divider

When a potential divider is used in electronic circuits, the output voltage signal is designed to operate another circuit. The output voltage in Fig 8.9(a) when there is no load will be 2.5 V, but, once it is connected to another circuit (the **load** in Fig 8.9(b)), the current drawn by the load, R_L, must be very small otherwise V_{OUT} will be reduced.

A simple calculation demonstrates this point. If $R_L = 1\,\text{k}\Omega$,

$$R_{parallel} = \frac{1}{\dfrac{1}{10} + \dfrac{1}{1}} = 0.9\,\text{k}\Omega$$

so

$$V_{OUT} = \frac{0.9\,\text{k}\Omega}{(10 + 0.9)\,\text{k}\Omega} \times 5\,\text{V} = 0.42\,\text{V}$$

With a much larger load resistance of $100\,\text{k}\Omega$, the resistance of the parallel circuit is now

$$R_{\text{parallel}} = \frac{1}{\dfrac{1}{10} + \dfrac{1}{100}} = 9\,\text{k}\Omega$$

So now

$$V_{\text{OUT}} = \frac{9\,\text{k}\Omega}{(10+9)\,\text{k}\Omega} \times 5\,\text{V} = 2.4\,\text{V}$$

which is much closer to the value calculated when there is no load. The current through the $100\,\text{k}\Omega$ resistor is about one-tenth of the current in the potential divider network when there is no load. If the load draws more current, V_{OUT} will decrease significantly. Therefore, to prevent the potential divider being unduly loaded, it is best to ensure that the output current from the divider is no more than 10% of the current in the divider itself. This is known as the **ten per cent rule.**

So using a value of the base current of $9.09 \times 10^{-2}\,\text{mA}$, we have

$$R_1 + R_2 = \frac{5\,\text{V}}{9.09 \times 10^{-2}\,\text{mA}} = 55\,\text{k}\Omega \tag{2}$$

Combining equations (1) and (2):

$$\frac{55\,\text{k}\Omega}{R_2} = 5.56$$

So

$$R_2 \approx 10\,\text{k}\Omega \qquad \text{and} \qquad R_1 \approx 45\,\text{k}\Omega$$

In practice, the nearest preferred value should be chosen for R_1, i.e. $47\,\text{k}\Omega$, and a potentiometer used to set the value of R_2.

Coupling capacitors

You will recall from Chapter 2 that a capacitor allows a.c. to pass but prevents d.c. This is the purpose of the coupling capacitors C_1 and C_2 in the common-emitter amplifier circuit of Fig 8.3. C_1 adds the small input a.c. signal to the d.c. signal provided by the bias resistors as illustrated in Fig 8.10, so that the combined signal is fed into the inverter. C_2 allows the a.c. part of the amplified signal to leave the system. The presence of the coupling capacitors explains the reason for the reduction in gain at low frequencies (Fig 8.2). At low frequencies the capacitive reactance is high, reducing the passage of low-frequency signals. In order to maintain voltage gain at low frequencies the capacitors have to have relatively large values and therefore they are often electrolytic types. (At high frequencies various stray capacitances in components other than capacitors and in conducting tracks on a circuit board which are close together can result in a reduction in the gain of an amplifier.)

Stabilised common-emitter amplifier

The circuit in Fig 8.3 is not very stable owing to its dependence on the d.c. gain of the amplifier, h_{FE}, which can change as the transistor warms up. The circuit can be stabilised by connecting a resistor between the emitter terminal and $0\,\text{V}$ as illustrated in Fig 8.11. It should be apparent from the following calculation that the a.c. gain of this stabilised common-emitter amplifier depends only on the values of the load resistor R_L and the emitter resistor R_E.

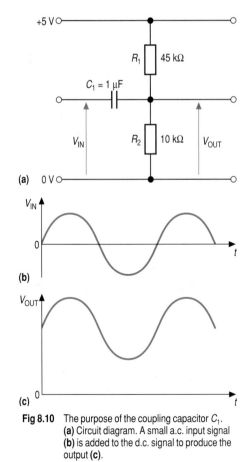

Fig 8.10 The purpose of the coupling capacitor C_1. (a) Circuit diagram. A small a.c. input signal (b) is added to the d.c. signal to produce the output (c).

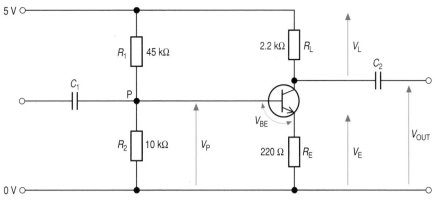

Fig 8.11 A fully stabilised common-emitter amplifier.

The derivation of the a.c. gain that follows assumes that the current through the potential divider network is much larger than the base current drawn from it, which means that the collector current and emitter current are approximately equal. The potential at P is

$$V_P = \frac{10}{45 + 10} \times 5 = 0.91 \, \text{V}$$

The p.d. across the base and emitter is 0.7 V. Therefore the p.d. across R_E must be 0.7 V below the potential at P, i.e.

$$V_E = 0.91 - 0.7 = 0.21 \, \text{V}$$

Assuming that $I_C = I_E$, then

$$\frac{V_L}{R_L} = \frac{V_E}{R_E}$$

Therefore

$$V_L = 0.21 \times \frac{2.2}{0.22} = 2.1 \, \text{V}$$

and

$$V_{OUT} = 5 - 2.1 = 2.9 \, \text{V}$$

If a small a.c. signal is applied to point P via a coupling capacitor, the increase in the voltage at the base will cause a corresponding increase in the voltage at the emitter. If the base signal increases by 0.2 V, we get $V_E = 0.41$ V. Therefore

$$V_L = 0.41 \times \frac{2.2}{0.22} = 4.1 \, \text{V}$$

and

$$V_{OUT} = 5 - 4.1 = 0.9 \, \text{V}$$

i.e. the output voltage has been reduced from 2.9 to 0.9 V (a drop of 2.0 V) when the input signal was increased by 0.2 V. Thus finally

$$\text{a.c. gain} = \frac{\Delta V_{OUT}}{\Delta V_{IN}} = \frac{-2.0 \, \text{V}}{0.2 \, \text{V}} = -10$$

The a.c. gain of this amplifier is −10, which is also the ratio of the load and emitter resistors. The voltage gain is due to the value of the load and emitter resistors and it can be shown that

$$\text{a.c. gain} = -\frac{R_L}{R_E}$$

Power dissipation in a transistor

One important difference you should have noticed about the amplifier circuit in Fig 8.11 compared with the amplifier circuit in Fig 8.3 where $V_{CE} \approx 0$ V at saturation is that there is now a substantial p.d. across the collector and emitter terminals (Fig 8.12), which means that the transistor will dissipate heat. The power dissipated by the transistor, P, is calculated from $P = I_C V_{CE}$. The power dissipated in this case is 0.95 mA $\times 2.69$ V $= 2.56$ mW. The maximum power rating for a BC108 is 300 mW, so it would not become too warm.

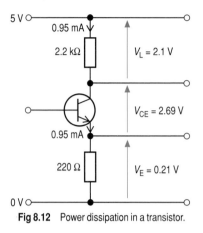

Fig 8.12   Power dissipation in a transistor.

If a transistor does heat up, its resistance decreases, allowing more current to pass. This causes the transistor to become even hotter until eventually the device is destroyed. This uncontrollable effect is known as **thermal runaway**. A transistor can be protected against the effect of thermal runaway by attaching a **heat sink** to it. Heat sinks are usually painted black and have fins to increase heat transfer away from the transistor by radiation and convection. The **thermal resistance** of the heat sink is a measure of its ability to transfer heat away from the transistor. The lower the thermal resistance, the better the heat sink. Very little heat is dissipated when a transistor is cut off or saturated. For this reason a transistor being operated as a switch should only be used at the cut-off and saturation voltages, because the larger currents involved in switching circuits would damage it if it is operated in the linear region.

8.4 MICROPHONES

The common-emitter amplifier described in the previous section is a small-signal amplifier which could act as the pre-amplifier input stage to our simple intercom system. When we connect up subsystems using signal sources we must make sure that the output of one circuit can feed in to the input of the next circuit properly, i.e. with no reduction in the size of the signal. In order to connect a microphone to the input of this amplifier, an appreciation of the types of microphone available and their impedances should be taken into account before we look at interfacing the microphone (signal source) to the pre-amplifier. A **microphone** is an input sensor which converts sound waves into electrical signals. Two of the most common types of microphone, dynamic and capacitor, are shown in Fig 8.13.

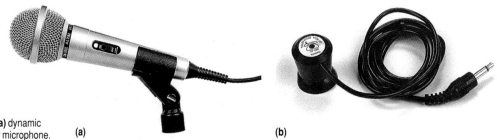

Fig 8.13   Two common microphones: **(a)** dynamic microphone and **(b)** capacitor microphone.

(a)   **(b)**

Dynamic or **moving-coil microphones** can have either low or high impedance. Some are designed to have both low and high impedance (typically $200\,\Omega$ to $50\,k\Omega$). This type of microphone is often **unidirectional**, which means that it is more sensitive to sound coming from a particular direction, and is suitable for use in public address systems and recording.

A **capacitor** or **condenser microphone** has a typical impedance of $600\,\Omega$ and is usually **omnidirectional**, which enables it to pick up sound from a wide angle. It is used where high sound quality is required, for example in concerts where sound must be received from various angles.

Crystal microphones have a high impedance of typically $1\,M\Omega$.

Microphone leads

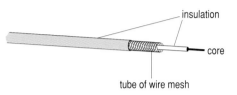

Fig 8.14 Screened audio cable.

Owing to the small signals generated by microphones, any interference which may distort the signal must be eliminated before the amplitude of the small signal is increased by the input stage of the amplifier. This is done by using screened leads (coaxial cable) between the microphone and the input. The conducting cable carrying the audio signal is insulated and then surrounded by a wire mesh as in Fig 8.14. The mesh is connected to earth at one point and screens the inner cable from any electrical interference.

8.5 IMPEDANCE REQUIREMENTS FOR THE INPUT STAGE

In Fig 8.11, it was assumed that the signal source had negligible impedance. If the bipolar transistor in Fig 8.11 is used to amplify the small signals generated by a high-impedance crystal microphone, problems arise because the impedance of the signal source is much greater than the impedance of the amplifier. The combined effect of the resistances of R_1 and R_2 and the capacitive reactance of C_1 provides the input impedance of the amplifier. It can be shown that this is equivalent to the effective parallel resistance of R_1 and R_2 if the frequency of the input signal is large enough for the capacitive reactance to be ignored. The circuit in Fig 8.11 would therefore have an input impedance of about $8\,k\Omega$. Fig 8.15(a) shows the equivalent impedance circuit for amplification of small signals generated by a microphone. V_S is the small voltage generated by the microphone, Z_S is the impedance of the microphone, Z_{IN} is the input impedance of the amplifier and V_{IN} is the input voltage to the amplifier. The circuit can be considered as a potential divider as in Fig 8.15(b):

$$V_{IN} = \frac{Z_{IN}}{Z_S + Z_{IN}} V_S$$

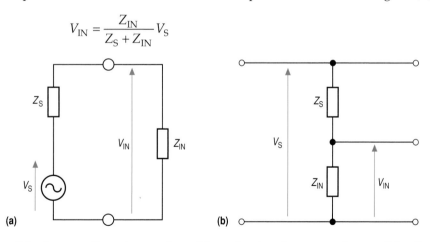

Fig 8.15 **(a)** Equivalent input impedance to amplify small signals from a microphone. **(b)** The circuit considered as a potential divider.

(a) (b)

Maximum voltage is **transferred** from the signal source to the amplifier (i.e. $V_S = V_{IN}$) if $Z_S \ll Z_{IN}$. The common-emitter amplifier circuit in Fig 8.11 is therefore only suitable for driving low-impedance dynamic microphones.

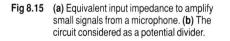

QUESTION

8.4 Using the circuit in Fig 8.15(b), calculate V_{IN} if $V_S = 20\,mV$, $Z_{IN} = 3\,k\Omega$ and $Z_S = 300\,\Omega$.

8.6 FET PRE-AMPLIFIERS

One of the advantages that field-effect transistors (FETs) have over bipolar transistors is their comparatively high input impedance. This makes the FET an ideal device for the first stage of an amplifier that is to receive its input signal from a high-impedance source such as a crystal microphone. A suitable pre-amplifier circuit using an n-channel JFET is shown in Fig 8.16. FET amplifiers have the advantage of high input impedance but the disadvantage of low gain; therefore the supply voltage used is higher than that used for the bipolar transistor to obtain a reasonable gain.

For this type of JFET the gate must be at a negative potential with respect to the source. This is achieved by **self-biasing** the transistor using resistors R_G and R_S. The gate is biased at 0 V by resistor R_G connected to 0 V. R_G is large to ensure that there is virtually no current in it and hence no p.d. across it. The drain current I_D produces a p.d. across the source resistor R_S and makes the source positive with respect to 0 V. Since $V_G = 0\,V$ and $V_S = I_D R_S$, the gate-to-source voltage is

$$V_{GS} = V_G - V_S = 0 - I_D R_S$$

i.e.

$$V_{GS} = -I_D R_S$$

A small a.c. signal passes through the coupling capacitor C_1 and makes the gate potential fluctuate, resulting in a varying drain current in the transistor. You will recall from Chapter 3 that the transconductance of a FET was defined as

$$g = \frac{\Delta I_D}{\Delta V_{GS}}$$

The a.c. voltage gain of the amplifier is defined as the ratio of change of output to change of input voltage. The following calculation illustrates how to determine the voltage gain:

$$\text{a.c. voltage gain} = \frac{\Delta V_{OUT}}{\Delta V_{IN}} = \frac{\Delta I_D R_S}{\Delta V_{GS} + \Delta V_S}$$

$$= \frac{\Delta I_D R_S}{\Delta V_{GS} + \Delta I_D R_S} = \frac{g \Delta V_{GS} R_S}{\Delta V_{GS} + g \Delta V_{GS} R_S}$$

which simplifies to

$$\text{a.c. voltage gain} = \frac{g R_S}{1 + g R_S}$$

If $g R_S$ is much greater than 1, then the gain of the amplifier will be about equal to 1. This circuit is called a source follower since the output is obtained from the source and it 'follows' the input because the gain of the amplifier is about equal to 1. Although this source follower does not produce any voltage gain, it is invaluable for connecting a high-impedance source with a low-impedance amplifier.

High-impedance sources

Other applications in which the signal source has a very high input impedance and the FET input stage is used are pH probes and biological probes used to probe muscle or nerve potentials.

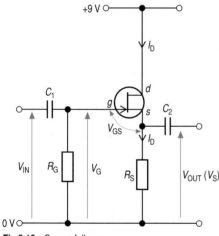

Fig 8.16 Source follower.

8.7 IMPEDANCE REQUIREMENTS FOR THE OUTPUT STAGE

The output impedance of the common-emitter amplifier is about equal to the load resistor in the collector circuit (i.e. $2.2\,k\Omega$ in Fig 8.11). This single-stage transistor amplifier is unable to drive a loudspeaker due to the fact that most loudspeakers have a low impedance (typically $8\,\Omega$) and the high output impedance of the common-emitter amplifier will not produce sufficient current to drive it. A current amplifier is needed as the next stage of the circuit. It can be shown that, for maximum transfer of power between two stages of a circuit, the output impedance of the first stage must be equal to the input impedance of the next stage. This is called **matching**.

Fig 8.17(a) shows the equivalent impedance circuit of an amplifier driving a loudspeaker. V is the amplified output voltage of the amplifier, Z_{OUT} is the output impedance of the amplifier, Z_L is the impedance of the load and V_{OUT} is the voltage across the load. The circuit can be considered as a potential divider as in Fig 8.17(b).

Maximum power is transferred when the power in the amplifier is equal to the power in the load:

$$I(V - V_{OUT}) = IV_{OUT}$$

i.e.

$$V = 2V_{OUT}$$

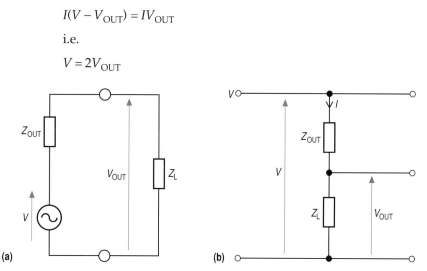

(a) **(b)**

Fig 8.17 **(a)** Equivalent output impedance to drive a loudspeaker. **(b)** The circuit considered as a potential divider.

The voltage across the output impedance of the amplifier must equal the voltage across the load. This is achieved when the impedances are matched, i.e. when

$$Z_{OUT} = Z_L$$

One way of achieving impedance matching is to use an emitter follower circuit, which is designed to have a high input impedance and a low output impedance.

8.8 POWER AMPLIFIERS

Transistor selection
The transistor used in the emitter follower should have a high power rating to ensure it can handle the high current in at the output stage.

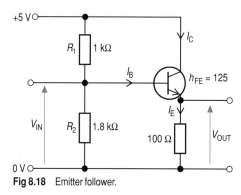

Fig 8.18 Emitter follower.

Emitter follower

In the emitter follower circuit shown in Fig 8.18, the collector terminal is connected to the positive supply and the emitter is connected through a resistor to 0 V. As the emitter voltage is always 0.7 V below the base voltage, the emitter will simply follow changes in the base voltage but will be 0.7 V behind.

The quiescent state is fixed by the resistors R_1 and R_2. When no a.c. signal is applied and with the component values given in Fig 8.18, the output voltage can be determined as follows:

$$V_{IN} = \frac{1.8}{1+1.8} \times 5\,V \approx 3.2\,V$$
$$V_{BE} = 0.7\,V$$

Therefore

$$V_{OUT} = 3.2 - 0.7 = 2.5\,V \qquad \text{(half the supply voltage)}$$

V_{OUT} is fixed to equal half the supply voltage in order to minimise the distortion. The voltage gain of the amplifier is therefore equal to 1 since any change in the input voltage will lead to a proportionate change in the output voltage.

Although the emitter follower does not amplify the voltage, it does amplify the current:

$$I_E = \frac{2.5\,\text{V}}{100\,\Omega} = 0.025\,\text{A} = 25\,\text{mA}$$

but $I_E \approx I_C$ since the collector current is much larger than the base current, and so

$$I_B = \frac{I_C}{h_{FE}} = \frac{25}{125} = 0.2\,\text{mA}$$

Then

$$\text{power input} = 3.2 \times 0.2 = 0.64\,\text{mW}$$
$$\text{power output} = 2.5 \times 25 = 62.5\,\text{mW}$$

giving a power gain of almost 100.

QUESTION

8.5 Calculate the following quantities for the circuit shown in Fig 8.19 (assume $V_{BE} = 0.7\,\text{V}$):
(a) the emitter voltage,
(b) the emitter current,
(c) the base current,
(d) the power dissipated by the transistor.

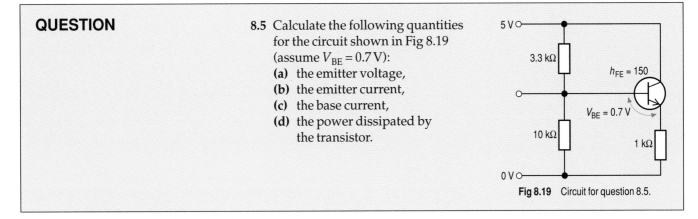

Fig 8.19 Circuit for question 8.5.

Darlington transistor

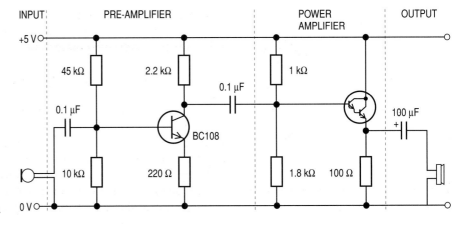

The power gain of an emitter follower can be increased using a **Darlington transistor**. These semiconductor devices contain two transistors in a single package. The schematic symbol for a Darlington transistor is shown in Fig 8.20. TR1 provides the base current for TR2. If the gain of each transistor is 100 and the base current for TR1 is 1 mA, then its collector current is 100 mA. For TR1, I_E is approximately equal to I_C since the base current is much smaller than the collector current. Therefore the collector current of TR1 provides the base current for TR2, resulting in a collector current of 10 000 mA for TR2. For the Darlington transistor:

$$\text{overall gain} = \text{product of individual gains} = h_{FE1} \times h_{FE2}$$

where h_{FE1} and h_{FE2} are the gains of TR1 and TR2 respectively.

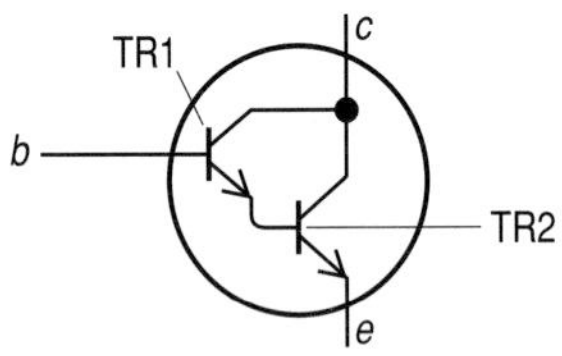

Fig 8.20 Darlington transistor symbol.

Fig 8.21 Audio amplifier circuit.

AUDIO AND RADIO SYSTEMS

An equivalent circuit can be constructed using two individual transistors, but the combined package is more convenient. The switch-on voltage for a silicon Darlington transistor is about 1.4 V since both transistors have to be switched on.

A practical circuit for our simple intercom system can now be constructed as in Fig 8.21.

Push–pull amplifiers

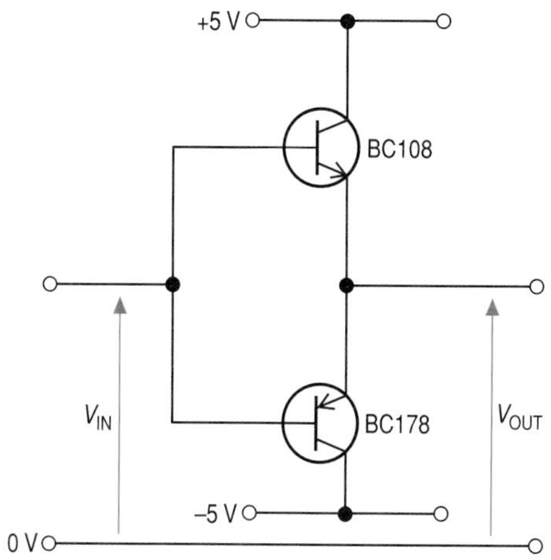

Push–pull amplifiers are sometimes used in the output stage of an amplifier to overcome any power dissipation problems which exist with the single-transistor emitter follower. A basic version shown in Fig 8.22 uses pnp and npn transistors arranged as a **push–pull** (or **complementary follower**) amplifier (note that a dual voltage supply is needed because of the presence of the pnp transistor). Both transistors are connected as emitter followers, which have a low input impedance designed to match the impedance of the load, so that maximum power is transferred. When an a.c. input signal is applied to the base of both transistors, the npn transistor conducts when the positive half of the input is greater than about 0.7 V, and the pnp transistor conducts when the negative half of the input is greater than −0.7 V. The term 'push–pull' is used because, when one transistor is on, the other is off. In this simple design, there is no steady current in the load so there are no power dissipation problems.

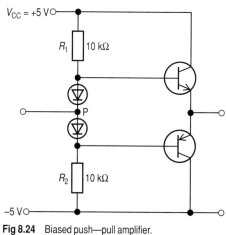

Fig 8.22 Push—pull amplifier.

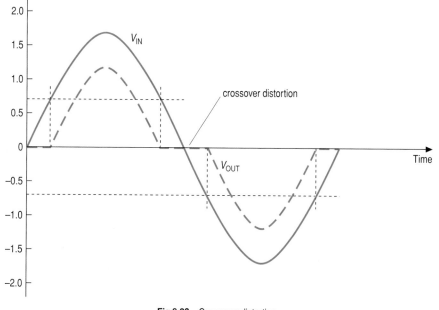

Fig 8.23 Crossover distortion.

The graphs in Fig 8.23 show that the output follows the input but the output is zero when the input lies within the range −0.7 V to +0.7 V. This leads to a cut-off zone called **crossover distortion.** This can be overcome by forward biasing the base–emitter junctions of both transistors so that small quiescent currents pass when no input signal is applied. This will result in the smallest input signal making the transistors conduct. One way of achieving this is to use a potential divider and diode arrangement as shown in Fig 8.24. The characteristics of the diodes and transistors must be closely matched. The resistors R_1 and R_2 are equal, so that the potential at P is equal to half the supply voltage. As a result the voltage across the emitters is also $\frac{1}{2}V_{CC}$. Although the cut-off zone will be reduced, there is now power dissipated by the transistors and the circuit is thermally unstable. The transistors used in a push–pull amplifier should be a **complementary pair** with identical gains, so

Fig 8.24 Biased push—pull amplifier.

that one half of the cycle is not amplified more than the other. Complementary pairs such as the BC108 and BC178 are often given in components catalogues.

8.9 EARPHONES AND LOUDSPEAKERS

Earphones and **loudspeakers** are output transducers which convert electrical energy into sound.

Magnetic or **moving-coil** type earphones have a low impedance, typically $8\,\Omega$, and the crystal type have a high impedance, typically $3\,M\Omega$. Earphones are used in deaf aids or in simple radio receivers.

The construction of a **moving-coil loudspeaker** is shown in Fig 8.25. Alternating current in the coil causes it to vibrate between the poles of a magnet. The coil is wound on a tube connected to a paper cone which vibrates the surrounding air to produce sound at the same frequencies as the alternating current in the coil. The impedance of a moving-coil loudspeaker is typically $8\,\Omega$.

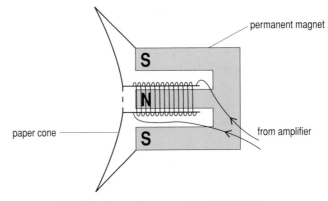

Fig 8.25   Construction of a moving-coil loudspeaker.

Its bandwidth, i.e. the frequency range for which the power gain does not fall below 3 dB of its maximum value, depends on a number of variables including the mass and diameter of the cone. 'Hi-fi' systems use **bass** or **woofer** loudspeakers which have large-diameter heavy cones designed to operate at low frequencies, typically 20 Hz to 2 kHz. **Treble** or **tweeter** loudspeakers have small-diameter light cones and are designed to operate at higher frequencies, typically 2 to 20 kHz. **Filters** are used to ensure that each speaker receives only its appropriate frequencies.

8.10 FILTERS

Filters are designed to pass some frequencies and reduce others.

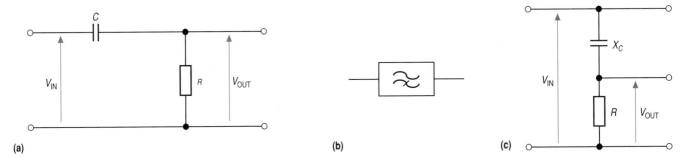

Fig 8.26   High-pass filter: **(a)** circuit and **(b)** symbol; **(c)** the circuit considered as a potential divider.

A simple RC **high-pass filter** circuit is shown in Fig 8.26(a), with its symbol being shown in Fig 8.26(b). The capacitor C, with reactance X_C, can be considered to be in series with the resistor R, forming a potential divider circuit as in Fig 8.26(c). The total impedance of the circuit, Z, is given by:

$$V_{OUT} = \frac{R}{Z}V_{IN} = \frac{R}{\sqrt{R^2 + X_C^2}}V_{IN} \quad \text{that is} \quad \frac{V_{OUT}^2}{V_{IN}^2} = \frac{R^2}{R^2 + X_C^2}$$

Capacitive reactance depends on frequency,

$$f = \frac{1}{2\pi X_C C}$$

When the frequency is such that the capacitive reactance has the same value as the resistance R, then

$$\frac{V_{OUT}^2}{V_{IN}^2} = \frac{R^2}{R^2 + R^2} = \frac{1}{2} \qquad \text{so} \qquad \frac{V_{OUT}}{V_{IN}} = 0.7$$

which corresponds to a power loss of $-3\,\text{dB}$. The frequency at which $X_C = R$ is called the **break frequency** f_0 and is given by the equation:

$$f_0 = \frac{1}{2\pi RC}$$

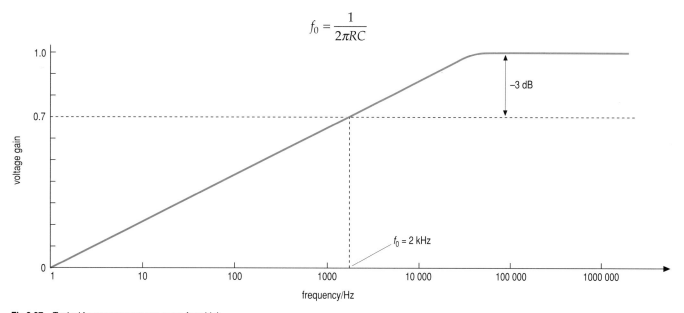

Fig 8.27 Typical frequency response curve for a high-pass filter.

The graph in Fig 8.27 shows the frequency response for a high-pass filter. For frequencies $f > f_0$, X_C will be less than R. For high frequencies, $X_C \ll R$, so

$$\frac{V_{OUT}^2}{V_{IN}^2} \approx \frac{R^2}{R^2} \approx 1$$

i.e. the voltage gain $V_{OUT}/V_{IN} \approx 1$. A tweeter loudspeaker is required to operate at frequencies above f_0.

A simple RC **low-pass filter** circuit is shown in Fig 8.28 together with its symbol.

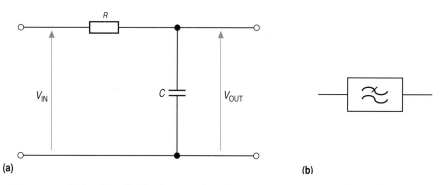

Fig 8.28 Low-pass filter: **(a)** circuit and **(b)** symbol

The graph in Fig 8.29 shows the frequency response for a low-pass filter. A woofer loudspeaker is required to operate at frequencies below f_0.

Recall: $X_C = \dfrac{1}{2\pi f C}$

and $X_L = 2\pi f L$

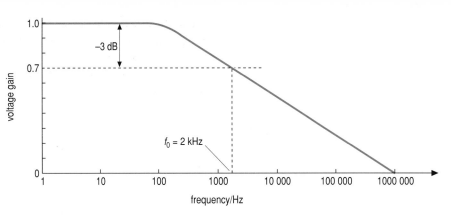

Fig 8.29   Typical frequency response curve for a low-pass filter.

To obtain a wide frequency response, tweeter and woofer loudspeakers are connected via a **crossover network** which uses a capacitor and inductor. A very simple crossover network circuit is shown in Fig 8.30. The capacitor allows high-frequency signals to pass to the tweeter and the inductor allows low-frequency signals to pass to the woofer. The complete speaker system is usually housed in a cabinet as in Fig 8.31. Careful enclosure design boosts the performance of the system considerably.

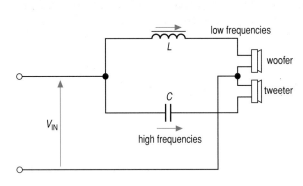

Fig 8.30   A simple crossover network.

Fig 8.31   Loudspeaker system.

8.11 RADIO SYSTEMS

All communication systems contain the same fundamental building blocks. The simple audio system described at the beginning of this chapter represents the receiver part of a communications system allowing information to be collected by the microphone and turned back into a sound wave by the loudspeaker. The information in this case is sent (transmitted) to the receiver directly as sound waves from the sender. The sound is **carried** by the air particles from the sender to the microphone and from the loudspeaker to the hearer. The information is **carried** between the various subsystems by means of electric currents in wires. In the case of a **radio system**, information is transmitted by radio waves, which are a form of **electromagnetic radiation**. Radio signals have much higher frequencies than audio signals. Radio waves are inaudible, so in order to transmit a.f. signals (such as speech and music) by radio, a technique called **modulation** is used where the information is carried or superimposed onto a high-frequency radio wave called a **carrier wave**.

There are two principal methods used for transmitting everyday music and entertainment programmes by radio. **Amplitude modulation (AM)** systems cause the amplitude of the carrier wave to be modulated by the audio signal. **Frequency modulation (FM)** systems modulate the carrier wave's frequency instead of the amplitude.

Fig 8.32 shows the audio-frequency (a.f.) and radio-frequency (r.f.) signals and modulated waveforms suitable for transmitting the audio signal by radio systems.

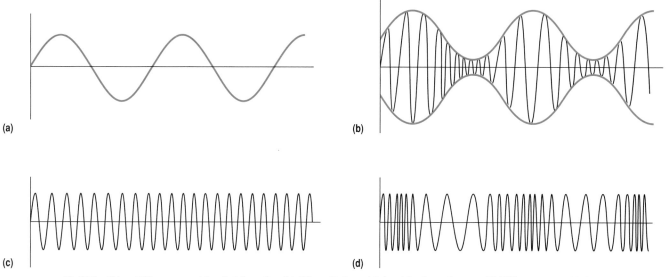

Fig 8.32   AM and FM processes: **(a)** audio information; **(b)** AM amplitude modulation; **(c)** radio carrier wave; **(d)** FM frequency modulation.

The problem with varying the amplitude of the carrier is that this enables unwanted information to interfere with the amplitude. Sources of electrical pulses, such as motors in electric food mixers, can cause unwanted amplitude peaks to be superimposed on the AM signal which is reproduced as 'crackling' interference on the receiver's loudspeaker. However FM systems do not take into account any variations in amplitude and therefore inherently reject more interference than AM systems.

Fig 8.33 shows a simplified block diagram of a complete AM radio communications system.

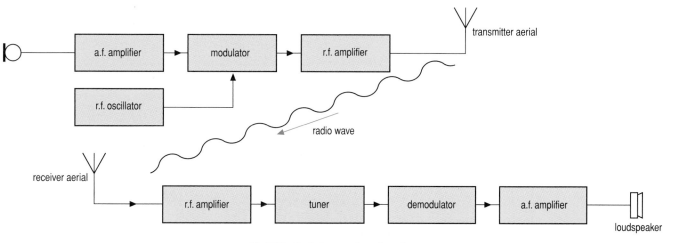

Fig 8.33   Block diagram of a radio system.

With the transmitter having placed the audio signal onto the carrier wave as variations in amplitude, the receiver must demodulate the signal to recover the original audio signal. Alternating currents produced in the aerial when a radio signal is received are fed to a tunable resonant circuit. Various other signals at different frequencies to the carrier wave will be picked up by the aerial and these unwanted signals must be rejected. When the resonant circuit is tuned to the frequency of the carrier wave, it resonates strongly and has an extremely high impedance for signals at this resonant frequency. This allows them to pass on to the next stage, but filters out other unwanted frequencies. The r.f. signal must then be rectified to produce a d.c. signal because otherwise the average signal level will be zero since the negative half-cycles match the positive half-cycles and will cancel out each other. A low-pass filter system then smooths out the rectified carrier signal to give the required output audio signal.

The earliest example of a radio receiver was the 'crystal set' shown in Fig 8.34.

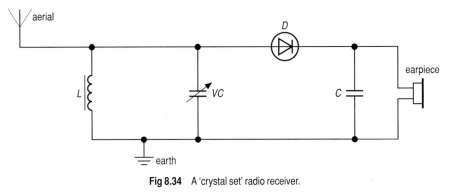

Fig 8.34 A 'crystal set' radio receiver.

If a high-impedance crystal earpiece is used as the output transducer, it is not necessary to amplify the signals. Each of the thousands of individual radio transmissions made at any one time must use only the legally allocated frequency for transmission and the receiver is then tuned to select the particular frequency from all those received by the aerial. The **tuning circuit** consists of an inductor and a variable capacitor. In Chapter 2 a series tuned circuit was considered which provided a low-impedance circuit when tuned at the resonant frequency. In the radio receiver circuit in Fig 8.34, the capacitor and inductor are connected in *parallel* which produces an extremely high impedance at the resonant frequency, the frequency at which the capacitive reactance is equal to the inductive reactance. The component values are such that the circuit has a low impedance for all frequencies *except* the **carrier frequency**, which is given by

$$f_0 = \frac{1}{2\pi\sqrt{LC}}$$

So the carrier frequency is prevented from passing to earth.

The sound wave must then be extracted from the radio wave. This is called **demodulation** and is achieved using a diode and a capacitor. The diode rectifies the signal so that only the positive half of the signal is conducted, and the capacitor filters out the high radio frequencies so that only the audio frequency is received by the loudspeaker. The capacitive reactance $X_C = 1/(2\pi f C)$ is low at high radio frequencies so these will be filtered to $0\,\text{V}$ whilst the lower audio frequencies will remain. The waveforms are shown in Figs 8.35 and 8.36.

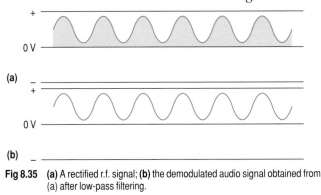

Fig 8.35 **(a)** A rectified r.f. signal; **(b)** the demodulated audio signal obtained from (a) after low-pass filtering.

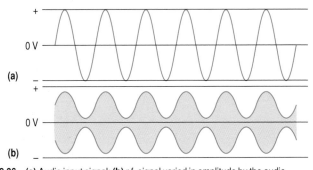

Fig 8.36 **(a)** Audio input signal; **(b)** r.f. signal varied in amplitude by the audio signal.

AUDIO AND RADIO SYSTEMS

The superhet receiver

One of the main problems of radio reception is that of selecting the required signal from a host of other signals. Most modern radio receivers are of the **superheterodyne** (superhet) type, which make use of the phenomenon of **beats**. Beats occur when two sound signals which are almost equal in frequency are combined. The resulting signal changes regularly in amplitude, resulting in a beating sound. The frequency of the beats is equal to the difference between the frequencies of the two signals being combined. The essential parts of a superhet receiver are illustrated as a block diagram in Fig 8.37. An oscillator generates a radio-frequency wave of frequency f_1 (usually at a frequency of 455 kHz above the station frequency, i.e. the frequency of the carrier) that is mixed with the incoming r.f. carrier wave of frequency f_2, thereby producing a radio-frequency wave of lower frequency called the **intermediate frequency** (IF), which is equal to $f_2 - f_1$ (455 kHz for most AM receivers). This is the new carrier frequency, which still has the a.f. signal amplitude modulated onto it. To tune the receiver to different frequencies, the frequency of the oscillations is changed, but the intermediate frequency always remains the same. The intermediate frequency is amplified before the audio-frequency signal is demodulated from the carrier as before.

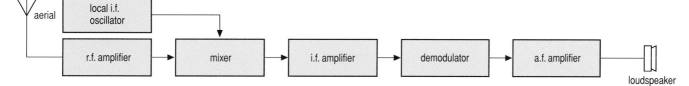

Fig 8.37 Block diagram of a 'superhet'.

Hi-fi systems

Fidelity is the equality of response of the receiver to various audio-frequency signals modulated on the carrier. Extremely high fidelity, which means a flat frequency response over the entire audible range from about 20 Hz to 20 kHz, is extremely difficult to obtain. A **high-fidelity** (hi-fi) system is no stronger than its weakest link, and the links include not only all the circuits in the receiver, but also the speaker(s), the acoustic properties of the room in which the speaker(s) are located, and the transmitter to which the receiver is tuned. Most AM radio stations do not reproduce faithfully sounds below 100 Hz or above 5 kHz; FM stations generally have a frequency range of 50 Hz to 15 kHz, the upper limit being set by Federal Communications Commission regulations.

SUMMARY

A microphone converts sound into electrical energy.

Maximum voltage is transferred between source and load when the impedance of the load is much greater than the impedance of the source. The input stage of an amplifier is designed to achieve maximum voltage transfer between the source and the amplifier.

Maximum power is transferred between source and load when the impedance of the load is equal to the impedance of the source (the impedances are matched).

A loudspeaker converts electrical energy into sound.

A filter transmits signals with frequencies within certain designated ranges.

An AM radio receiver picks up radio frequencies, selects the correct frequency and then extracts the audio signal from the modulated radio frequency to produce sound in a loudspeaker.

Chapter 9

THE OPERATIONAL AMPLIFIER

LEARNING OBJECTIVES

After studying this chapter you should be able to:

1. describe the properties of an ideal operational amplifier;

2. understand the principles of negative and positive feedback in an amplifier;

3. draw the circuit diagrams for inverting and non-inverting amplifiers;

4. derive and use expressions for the voltage gain of inverting and non-inverting amplifiers;

5. describe the use of an operational amplifier as a voltage follower, difference amplifier, summing amplifier, comparator, ramp generator, Schmitt trigger and oscillator.

9.1 OPERATIONAL AMPLIFIERS

The advent of the operational amplifier (op-amp) has provided the electronic circuit designer with another means of amplifying low-level analogue signals. The **operational amplifier** is an example of an **analogue** (or **linear**) integrated circuit which offers near-ideal characteristics, i.e. virtually infinite voltage gain with low output resistance and wide bandwidth. The name originates from the use of operational amplifiers to perform mathematical *operations* (calculations) in analogue computers which are now obsolete, having been replaced by much faster digital computers. The operational amplifier IC is still the basic building block of an analogue system used widely in instrumentation and control systems. Such is the versatility of this IC that this chapter is devoted to the function and applications of the operational amplifier.

Practical work

The op-amp circuits considered in this chapter can be constructed on a breadboard or, alternatively, can be investigated using commercial boards. One such board is 'The London Operational Amplifier Board' shown in Fig 9.1, which is available from Unilab suppliers.

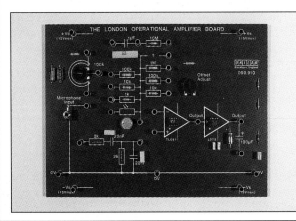

Fig 9.1   London Operational Amplifier Board.

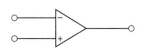

Fig 9.2 Operational amplifier (op-amp) symbol.

Terminology

The symbol for an op-amp is shown in Fig 9.2. The polarity markings of the inputs have nothing to do with the supply connections and, to avoid confusion, supply connections are rarely shown on circuit diagrams. The '+' input is known as the non-inverting input and the '−' as the inverting input. Most op-amps require a dual (or split) symmetrical power supply $(+V, 0\,V, -V)$ as shown in Fig 9.3. Some can operate from a single $(+V, 0\,V)$ supply. Throughout this chapter, V_1 **will refer to the voltage signal at the inverting input and** V_2 **to the voltage signal at the non-inverting input**

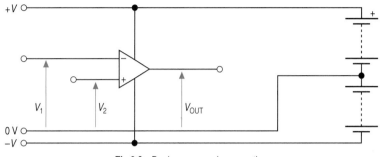

Fig 9.3 Dual power supply connections.

Definition of some common terms associated with operational amplifiers:

- The **open-loop voltage gain** is defined as the ratio of output to input voltage measured with no feedback applied. It is the d.c. gain of the amplifier or the gain at a frequency of 1 Hz.
- The **closed-loop voltage gain** is defined as the ratio of output to input voltage measured with feedback applied.
- The **bandwidth** is defined as the frequency range over which the gain does not fall by more than 3 dB from its mid-band value.

Characteristics of op-amps

The *ideal* op-amp should have the following characteristics:

- Infinite open-loop voltage gain.
- Infinite input impedance so that no current is drawn by the op-amp.
- Zero output impedance so that maximum current can be transferred to any load resistance.
- Very large bandwidth.

There are many types of **op-amp** IC available but the 081 FET is an inexpensive general-purpose type which will suit the applications suggested in this chapter. The pin connections for the 081 are shown in Fig 9.4, and its characteristics are listed in Table 9.1.

Table 9.1 Characteristics of 081 FET op-amp

Supply voltage range (V)	±5 to ±18
Open-loop gain (dB)	106
Input bias current (pA)	30
Slew rate (V µs^{-1})	13
Output voltage swing measured with ±15 V supply (V)	±13.5

Fig 9.4 Pin connections for the 081 FET op-amp.

The circuit diagrams illustrated in this chapter assume the use of the 081 op-amp connected to ±15 V.

An **op-amp amplifies the difference between its two input voltage signals**, V_1 and V_2. Fig 9.5 shows the voltage characteristic curve for a typical op-amp (with a supply voltage of $\pm15\,$V).

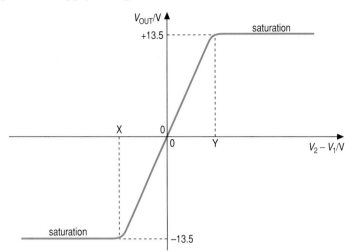

Fig 9.5 Typical voltage characteristic curve for an op-amp.

If the open-loop gain of an op-amp is A_{OL} then the output voltage is given by the equation:

$$V_{OUT} = A_{OL}(V_2 - V_1)$$

The open-loop voltage gain is very large, typically 200 000 (often expressed in dB, i.e. 106 dB), limiting the size of the linear region where the input voltage is proportional to the output voltage. Inputs outside this linear range cause **saturation**. The output voltage can never be more than the supply voltage V_S, so the output saturates close to the maximum value it can have, $+V_S$ or $-V_S$ in theory, but in practice the output of a typical op-amp can only get to within 1.5–2 V of the supply rails.

The gradient of the linear part of the graph is equal to the open-loop voltage gain A_{OL}. If $A_{OL} = 200\,000$ then at point Y on the graph,

$$V_2 - V_1 = \frac{13.5\,\text{V}}{200\,000} = 6.75 \times 10^{-5}\,\text{V} = 67.5\,\mu\text{V}$$

and at point X

$$V_2 - V_1 = -67.5\,\mu\text{V}$$

Therefore the **maximum input voltage swing** that can be amplified is only 135 μV before the op-amp saturates. This is not practicable for amplifying circuits since any reasonable size of input voltage would be amplified so much that **clipping** would occur and distort the signal. To use the op-amp as an amplifier, the gain must be reduced using **feedback**. The high gain of the op-amp is made use of in **switching circuits** such as the comparator.

9.2 THE COMPARATOR

When an op-amp is used in open-loop mode it acts as a **comparator**. A comparator compares the size of the two input voltages and, due to its high gain, gives an output close to the positive supply or to the negative supply voltage depending on which input is bigger.

- If V_2 is greater than V_1, then V_{OUT} is almost equal to the positive supply voltage, $+V_S$.
- If V_1 is greater than V_2, then V_{OUT} is almost equal to the negative supply voltage, $-V_S$.

($V_2 - V_1$ must be greater than 135 μV for saturation to occur.)

THE OPERATIONAL AMPLIFIER

This is useful if light- or temperature-sensing units, which produce analogue outputs, are required to provide digital output signals. If the analogue signal is fed into one input of the comparator and a reference voltage (provided by a potential divider) is connected to the other input, the output of the comparator will switch to a digital output state depending on which input is bigger. The reference voltage can be adjusted to determine the desired switching point. Fig 9.6 illustrates the use of a comparator as a light-operated switch.

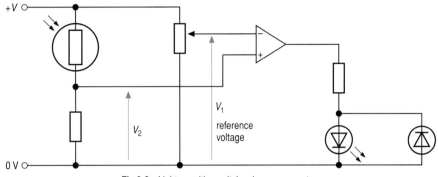

Fig 9.6 Light-sensitive switch using a comparator.

Suppose that the reference voltage is adjusted using the potential divider so that initially $V_2 = V_1$. When light falls on the LDR, its resistance decreases causing V_2 to increase. V_2 will be greater than V_1, causing the output to saturate at logic 1 and the LED will switch on. A diode is connected across the LED as shown in Fig 9.6 to protect it from the reverse voltage when the op-amp output saturates at −13.5 V, which is greater than the reverse voltage rating of an LED.

When an op-amp is used as a voltage comparator, the output takes time to switch from one state to another – this is called the **slew rate**. The 081 has a slew rate of $13\,V\,\mu s^{-1}$ which means that it takes about $2\,\mu s$ for the output to switch from −13.5 V to +13.5 V.

Further applications of comparators

A refrigerator used to store soft fruit in a warehouse must be kept at a temperature between 3.5 and 5.5 °C. A thermistor is used to measure the refrigerator temperature. It has a resistance of $4.0\,k\Omega$ at 3.5 °C and $3.7\,k\Omega$ at 5.5 °C. Fig 9.7 shows how two comparators can be used with the thermistor to produce the temperature control circuit. Protection diodes (not shown in Fig 9.7) are connected across each LED.

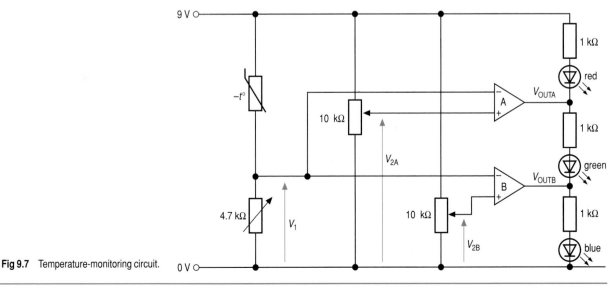

Fig 9.7 Temperature-monitoring circuit.

As the temperature of the thermistor falls, its resistance increases, causing V_1 to decrease. Using potential divider theory, it can be seen that V_1 will vary between 5.0 V at 5.5 °C and 4.9 V at 3.5 °C. The reference voltages are adjusted so that they are equal to these two extremes. Table 9.2 illustrates quantitatively what happens in this circuit when the temperature changes.

Table 9.2   Results for the temperature-monitoring circuit

Temperature/°C	Comparator A			Comparator B			LEDs		
	V_1/V	V_{2A}/V	V_{OUTA}/V	V_1/V	V_{2B}/V	V_{OUTB}/V	Red	Green	Blue
<3.5	<4.9	5.0	+13.5	<4.9	4.9	+13.5	Off	Off	On
3.5–5.5	4.9–5.0	5.0	+13.5	4.9–5.0	4.9	−13.5	Off	On	Off
>5.5	>5.0	5.0	−13.5	>5.0	4.9	−13.5	On	Off	Off

When the temperature falls below 3.5 °C the blue LED will light. When the temperature is within the correct temperature range of 3.5 to 5.5 °C the green LED will light. When the temperature rises above 5.5 °C the red LED will light.

QUESTION

9.1 Fig 9.8 shows part of a circuit used in an audio system to indicate the strength of a signal. Protection diodes (not shown) are connected across each LED. The stronger the incoming voltage signal, the greater the number of LEDs that light up. Explain how this system works.

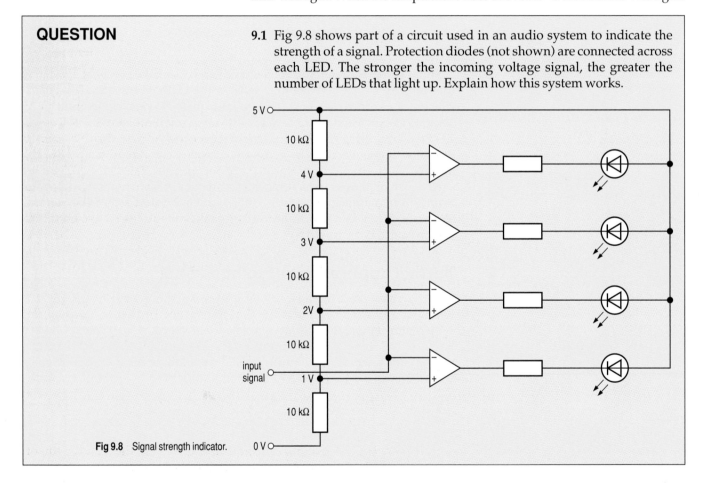

Fig 9.8   Signal strength indicator.

In practice, the arrangement drawn in Fig 9.8 uses **LED bar arrays** as in Fig 9.9, which can be driven from special LED bar driver ICs (LM3914 is an example).

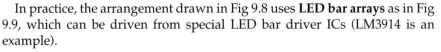

Fig 9.9   LED bar array.

THE OPERATIONAL AMPLIFIER

9.3 FREQUENCY RESPONSE

The frequency response curve in Fig 9.10 shows the relationship between the open-loop gain of a typical op-amp and the frequency of the input signal.

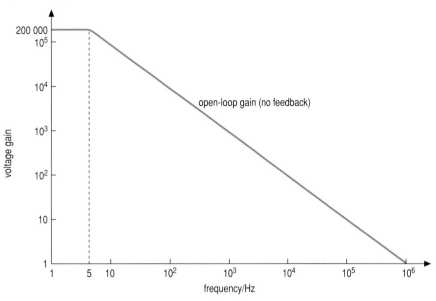

Fig 9.10 Typical op-amp frequency response curve.

At low frequencies where the gain is constant, the gain is so high that a very small input voltage swing will produce a saturated output; this is made use of in comparator circuits. The range of frequencies over which the gain is constant (the 'flat' part of the graph) represents the **bandwidth at −3 dB**, i.e. the frequency range over which the gain does not fall below 0.7 of its maximum value. For an op-amp with the frequency response in Fig 9.10, the bandwidth extends from 1 Hz to about 5 Hz, which is useless if it is to be used as an audio amplifier. To use an op-amp as an audio amplifier, the bandwidth must be increased to include the audio-frequency range 20 Hz to 20 kHz. The bandwidth can be calculated if the **unity-gain bandwidth** of the op-amp is known. This is the frequency at which the gain is 1, typically 1 MHz (or 10^6 Hz) (see Fig 9.10). Thus

$$\text{unity-gain bandwidth, } GB = \text{gain, } A \times \text{bandwidth, } B$$

Example: Prove that the bandwidth for the op-amp having the frequency response as in Fig 9.10 is 5 Hz when the d.c. gain is 200 000.
From the formula we have

$$\text{bandwidth, } B = \frac{GB}{A} = \frac{10^6}{200\,000} = 5\,\text{Hz}$$

The following calculations illustrate the effect on the bandwidth of reducing the gain. If the gain is reduced to 1000, the bandwidth B is

$$B = \frac{GB}{A} = \frac{10^6}{10^3} = 10^3\,\text{Hz} = 1\,\text{kHz} \qquad \text{(see Fig 9.11)}$$

If the gain is reduced to 100, then

$$B = \frac{GB}{A} = \frac{10^6}{100} = 10^4\,\text{Hz} = 10\,\text{kHz} \qquad \text{(see Fig 9.11)}$$

Fig 9.11 illustrates the effect on bandwidth of reducing the gain. The feedback fraction β, marked on the graphs, is defined in the next section.

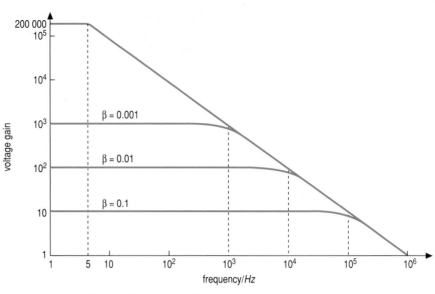

Fig 9.11   Effect on bandwidth of an op-amp when gain is reduced.

In order to widen the bandwidth, the gain of the op-amp must be reduced; this is achieved using **negative feedback**.

9.4 NEGATIVE FEEDBACK

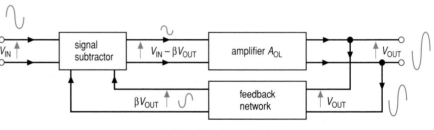

Fig 9.12   Negative feedback.

Most practical amplifiers use negative feedback in order to control the gain precisely and to increase the bandwidth. The amount of feedback employed determines the closed-loop gain.

The block diagram in Fig 9.12 demonstrates the action of negative feedback in an amplifier which has an open-loop gain, A_{OL}. A fraction β of the output voltage is fed back to the input. The output signal is in **antiphase** (180° out of phase) with the input signal so the feedback voltage is negative. If the input voltage (before feedback) is V_{IN} and the feedback voltage is βV_{OUT}, where V_{OUT} is the output voltage, then the effective input voltage to the amplifier will be reduced and is equal to $V_{IN} - \beta V_{OUT}$. Then the open-loop gain is

$$A_{OL} = \frac{V_{OUT}}{V_{IN} + \beta V_{OUT}}$$

$$V_{OUT} = A_{OL}V_{IN} + A_{OL}\beta V_{OUT}$$

$$V_{OUT}(1 - \beta A_{OL}) = A_{OL}V_{IN}$$

This rearranges to

$$\frac{V_{OUT}}{V_{IN}} = \frac{A_{OL}}{1 + \beta A_{OL}}$$

where V_{OUT}/V_{IN} is defined as the closed-loop gain, A_{CL}:

$$A_{CL} = \frac{A_{OL}}{1 + \beta A_{OL}}$$

THE OPERATIONAL AMPLIFIER

Example: If the negative-feedback fraction to an 081 op-amp is $\beta = 0.001$ and the open-loop gain is $A_{OL} = 200\,000$, calculate the closed-loop gain.
From the formula we have

$$A_{CL} = \frac{A_{OL}}{1 + \beta A_{OL}} = \frac{200\,000}{1 + 0.001 \times 200\,000} \approx 1000 \qquad \text{(see Fig 9.11)}$$

QUESTION

9.2 Calculate the closed-loop gain for an 081 when the negative-feedback fraction is **(a)** 0.01 and **(b)** 0.1. (The 081 has an open-loop gain of 200 000.)

There are two basic amplifying circuits for an op-amp which use negative feedback to reduce the open-loop gain: the non-inverting and inverting amplifiers.

Non-inverting amplifier

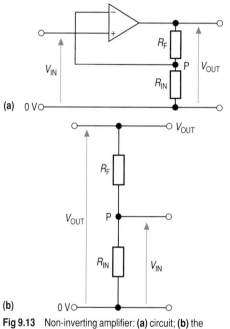

(a)

(b)

Fig 9.13 Non-inverting amplifier: **(a)** circuit; **(b)** the circuit considered as a potential divider.

The following formulae derived for these circuits assume that the op-amp behaves ideally – refer to the ideal characteristics in section 9.1.

Fig 9.13(a) shows a typical **non-inverting amplifier** circuit. The input voltage signal V_{IN} is applied to the non-inverting input. Since the open-loop gain of the op-amp is infinite, the input voltage to the op-amp, $V_2 - V_1 = 0$. If there is no p.d. between the inputs of the op-amp, then the voltage at point P is also equal to V_{IN}. No current is drawn by the inverting input so the current in R_{IN} is equal to the current in R_F. It is simpler to understand if the two resistors are considered as a potential divider circuit as in Fig 9.13(b). Then we can use the formula from potential divider theory:

$$V_{IN} = \frac{R_{IN}}{R_F + R_{IN}} V_{OUT}$$

$$\frac{V_{OUT}}{V_{IN}} = \frac{R_F + R_{IN}}{R_{IN}}$$

So the closed-loop voltage gain for a non-inverting amplifier is

$$A_{CL} = 1 + \frac{R_F}{R_{IN}}$$

QUESTION

9.3 If R_{IN} in Fig 9.13(a) has a value of $10\,k\Omega$, what value should be used for R_F to produce a voltage gain of 5? If the supply voltage is $\pm 15\,V$, calculate the output voltage when the input voltage is **(a)** $3\,mV$, **(b)** $0.5\,V$ and **(c)** $3.0\,V$. (The saturation voltage for the 081 is $\pm 13.5\,V$.)

Inverting amplifier

A typical circuit is shown in Fig 9.14. An ideal op-amp draws no current from the signal source, so the same current I flows through the input resistor R_{IN} and the feedback resistor R_F. The non-inverting input is connected to $0\,V$; therefore point P is also at $0\,V$ since $V_2 - V_1 = 0$. P is called the **virtual earth point**.

'Offset null'

In practice, the op-amp will draw a small input current and $V_2 - V_1$ is not zero (**input offset voltage** is typically of the order of microvolts). Therefore the voltage at P will not be zero, but nearly zero; hence the name 'virtual earth'. Pin 5 of the 081 is the '**offset null**', which can be used to adjust this **d.c. offset**. The offset connection is shown in Fig 9.15. VR is adjusted so that V_{OUT} is zero when no input voltage is applied.

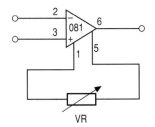

Fig 9.15 Offset connection.

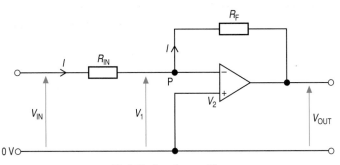

Fig 9.14 Inverting amplifier.

Since P is at 0 V, the p.d. across R_{IN} is

$$V_{IN} = IR_{IN}$$

and the p.d. across R_F is

$$-V_{OUT} = IR_F$$

Therefore

$$-\frac{V_{OUT}}{V_{IN}} = \frac{IR_F}{IR_{IN}}$$

and the closed-loop gain is

$$A_{CL} = \frac{V_{OUT}}{V_{IN}} = -\frac{R_F}{R_{IN}}$$

The value of R_{IN} should be high to prevent too much current being drawn from the signal source.

QUESTION

9.4 If R_{IN} in Fig 9.14 has a value of $10\,\text{k}\Omega$, what value should be used for R_F to produce a voltage gain of -10? If the supply voltage is $\pm15\,\text{V}$, calculate the output voltage when the input voltage is **(a)** $1\,\text{mV}$, **(b)** $0.5\,\text{mV}$ and **(c)** $1.5\,\text{V}$. (The saturation voltage for the 081 is $\pm13.5\,\text{V}$.)

INVESTIGATION

The inverting amplifier

Basic apparatus: breadboard; 081 op-amp; $4.7\,\text{k}\Omega$ potentiometer; digital voltmeter (DVM); dual power supply (±5 to $\pm15\,\text{V}$).

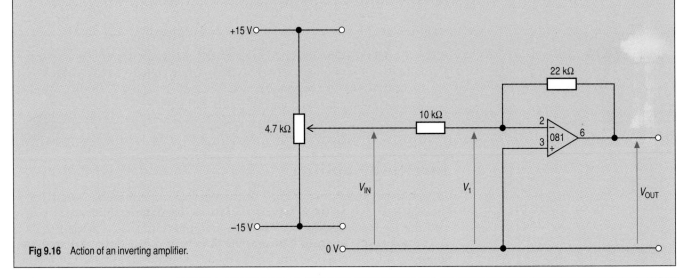

Fig 9.16 Action of an inverting amplifier.

THE OPERATIONAL AMPLIFIER

Construct the inverting amplifier circuit (Fig 9.16) on a breadboard. Use the potentiometer as shown in Fig 9.16 to vary the input voltage. Record the output voltage. Take suitable readings to plot a graph of V_{IN} against V_{OUT}.

Measure the closed-loop gain of the amplifier from the linear section of the graph. What is the maximum output voltage (positive and negative) when saturation occurs?

Replace the feedback resistor with a $33\,k\Omega$ resistor and repeat the experiment.

Set up a similar circuit for the non-inverting amplifier and repeat the experiment.

9.5 BASIC OPERATIONAL AMPLIFIER CIRCUITS THAT USE NEGATIVE FEEDBACK

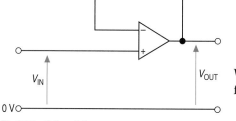

Fig 9.17 Voltage follower.

The voltage follower

Op-amps have a high input impedance and a low output impedance, enabling them to be used to match a high-impedance signal source to a low-impedance load.

The op-amp circuit used for this purpose is the **voltage follower**, which is simply a **unity-gain non-inverting amplifier** with a gain of 1 as shown in Fig 9.17.

The closed-loop gain of the non-inverting amplifier is

$$A_{CL} = \frac{A_{OL}}{1 + \beta A_{OL}}$$

When the output is connected directly to the inverting input, the feedback fraction $\beta = 1$ since all of the output is fed back to the input. Then

$$A_{CL} = \frac{A_{OL}}{1 + A_{OL}}$$

Since the open-loop gain A_{OL} is large

$$A_{CL} \approx \frac{A_{OL}}{A_{OL}} \approx 1$$

The closed-loop gain is 1, which means that the output signal is the same as the input (the output 'follows' the input).

Although the voltage is not amplified, the circuit can be used to match a high-impedance signal source with a low-impedance load. This type of circuit is often called a **buffer amplifier**.

The voltage follower can be used with a capacitor to make a **coulombmeter**, as illustrated in Fig 9.18. This circuit is useful because, if a voltmeter is used to measure the p.d. across a charged capacitor, charge flows from the capacitor through the voltmeter, discharging the capacitor and making measurements impossible.

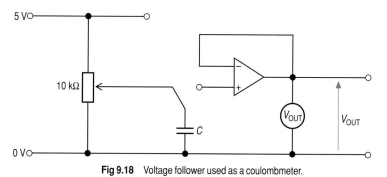

Fig 9.18 Voltage follower used as a coulombmeter.

The capacitor is charged from the potentiometer, then connected to the non-inverting input of the op-amp. Ideally there is no p.d. across the inputs of the op-amp and the voltage at the inverting input is the same as the output voltage, V_{OUT}. Therefore the voltage across the capacitor is also equal to V_{OUT}. The op-amp has a very high input impedance, so no charge flows from the capacitor to the op-amp input. Therefore V_{OUT} remains steady even if the voltmeter has a resistance as low as $1\,k\Omega$. The charge on the capacitor is CV_{OUT}.

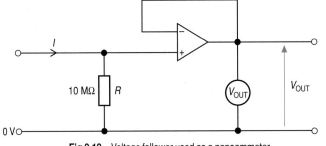

Fig 9.19 Voltage follower used as a nanoammeter.

The voltage follower can also be used as a **nanoammeter**. Fig 9.19 shows how it can measure very small currents of the order of nanoamperes ($1\,nA = 10^{-9}\,A$). The voltmeter records the p.d. across the large-value resistor. If the voltmeter has a full-scale deflection of $100\,mV$ and the smallest measurable deflection is $2\,mV$, then the smallest current I that can be measured is

$$I = \frac{V_{OUT}}{R} = \frac{2 \times 10^{-3}}{10 \times 10^{6}} = 0.2 \times 10^{-9}\,A = 0.2\,nA$$

Difference amplifier

A **difference amplifier** finds the difference between the two input signals. A typical difference amplifier circuit is shown in Fig 9.20.

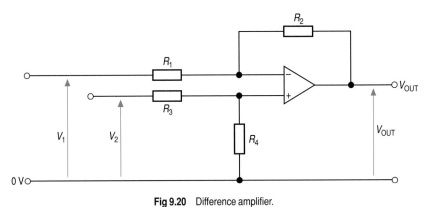

Fig 9.20 Difference amplifier.

If $R_1 = R_3$ and $R_2 = R_4$ it can be shown that

$$V_{OUT} = \frac{R_2}{R_1}(V_2 - V_1)$$

If all four resistors in Fig 9.20 have the same value, then $V_{OUT} = V_2 - V_1$; the circuit has a gain of 1 and determines the difference between the two input voltages.

Summing amplifier

This is a type of inverting amplifier circuit and is often used in digital-to-analogue conversion (see Chapter 10) or as a **'mixer'** in audio systems to combine signals from more than one source. The **inverting summing amplifier** circuit is shown in Fig 9.21.

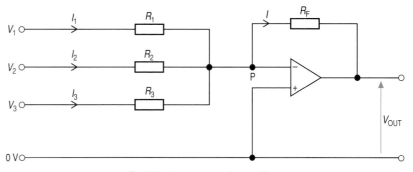

Fig 9.21 Inverting summing amplifier.

The non-inverting input is connected to 0 V; therefore point P will be at 0 V (virtual earth point). For this circuit

$$I = I_1 + I_2 + I_3$$

$$-\frac{V_{OUT}}{R_F} = \frac{V_1}{R_1} + \frac{V_2}{R_2} + \frac{V_3}{R_3}$$

$$-V_{OUT} = \left(V_1 \times \frac{R_F}{R_1} + V_2 \times \frac{R_F}{R_2} + V_3 \times \frac{R_F}{R_3} \right)$$

If $R_1 = R_2 = R_3 = R_F$ then

$$V_{OUT} = -(V_1 + V_2 + V_3)$$

In this case, the output is the sum of the input signals but is of opposite polarity.

Integrator

Fig 9.22 shows the circuit diagram for a basic **integrator**. It is commonly used as a **ramp generator** to convert a steady input voltage signal into a voltage which varies linearly with time. This circuit is used in digital voltmeter circuits (see Chapter 10).

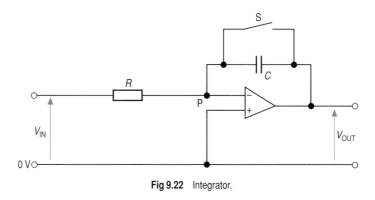

Fig 9.22 Integrator.

With switch S open, the current through R is V_{IN}/R, which charges the capacitor C. After time t the charge Q on the capacitor is $(V_{IN}/R)\,t$. This gives

$$V_{OUT} = -\frac{Q}{C} = -\frac{V_{IN}}{CR} t$$

where CR is the time constant. If $C = 1\,\mu F$ and $R = 100\,k\Omega$ then $CR = 0.1\,s$. If $V_{IN} = +0.5\,V$ then $V_{OUT}/t = -0.5/0.1 = -5.0\,V\,s^{-1}$.

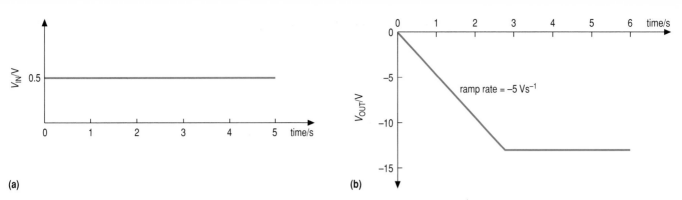

(a)

(b)

Fig 9.23 **(a)** Input and **(b)** output graphs for a ramp rate of $-5\ \mathrm{V\ s^{-1}}$.

Fig 9.23 illustrates how the output of the ramp generator circuit in Fig 9.22 changes with time when the input voltage is a steady $0.5\ \mathrm{V}$. V_{OUT} can be reset to $0\ \mathrm{V}$ by closing the switch S. The non-inverting input is at $0\ \mathrm{V}$. Therefore the voltage at P is $0\ \mathrm{V}$; so when S is closed, the capacitor is discharged and V_{OUT} will be $0\ \mathrm{V}$. The ramp can be reset using a transistor connected as shown in Fig 9.24. When the transistor switches on, the capacitor discharges through R_{L}.

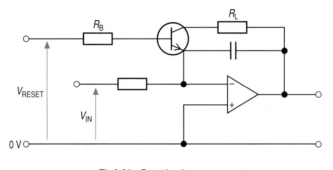

Fig 9.24 Resetting the ramp generator.

9.6 POSITIVE FEEDBACK

An alternative form of feedback, where the output is fed back in such a way that it reinforces the input, is known as **positive feedback**.

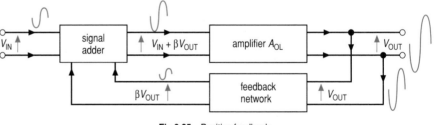

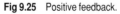

Fig 9.25 Positive feedback.

The block diagram in Fig 9.25 demonstrates the action of **positive feedback** in an amplifier which has an open-loop gain of A_{OL}. A fraction β of the output, is fed back to the input. The output signal is in phase with the input signal, so the feedback voltage is $+\beta V_{\mathrm{OUT}}$. Then the open-loop gain is

$$A_{\mathrm{OL}} = \frac{V_{\mathrm{OUT}}}{V_{\mathrm{IN}} + \beta V_{\mathrm{OUT}}}$$

$$V_{\mathrm{OUT}} = A_{\mathrm{OL}}V_{\mathrm{IN}} + A_{\mathrm{OL}}\beta V_{\mathrm{OUT}}$$

$$V_{\mathrm{OUT}}(1 - \beta A_{\mathrm{OL}}) = A_{\mathrm{OL}}V_{\mathrm{IN}}$$

THE OPERATIONAL AMPLIFIER

So in this case the closed-loop gain is

$$A_{\mathrm{CL}} = \frac{V_{\mathrm{OUT}}}{V_{\mathrm{IN}}} = \frac{A_{\mathrm{OL}}}{1 - \beta A_{\mathrm{OL}}}$$

Positive feedback is *not* used in amplifying circuits because the gain of the amplifier is so high that even very small-voltage input signals will cause the output to saturate and distort the waveform being amplified. Positive feedback is used in **Schmitt trigger** and **oscillator** circuits.

Schmitt trigger

A basic comparator switching circuit is illustrated in Fig 9.6. When V_2 rises above the reference voltage V_1, the output saturates at +13.5 V. When V_2 falls below V_1, the output saturates at −13.5 V. The disadvantage of this circuit is that the output is likely to 'jitter' when it is about to switch off or on due to small changes in the voltage inputs V_1 and V_2 caused by electrical noise. This can be overcome using positive-feedback Schmitt trigger circuits.

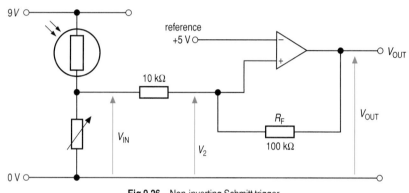

Fig 9.26   Non-inverting Schmitt trigger.

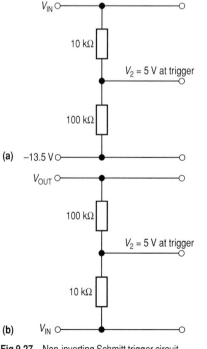

A **non-inverting Schmitt trigger** circuit is shown in Fig 9.26. Positive feedback is achieved via resistor R_{F}. Therefore the output will be saturated.

Assume that V_{OUT} is initially −13.5 V, which means that the non-inverting input V_2 must be less than the reference voltage +5 V. As the LDR is illuminated, its resistance decreases and V_{IN} increases. Once V_2 rises above 5 V, the output will rise rapidly to +13.5 V due to the positive feedback. The trigger voltage V_{IN} at which the output changes state can be calculated using potential divider theory. It is easier to understand if the circuit is considered as a potential divider as in Fig 9.27(a). From potential divider theory

$$5 - (-13.5) = \frac{100}{10 + 100}\left[V_{\mathrm{IN}} - (-13.5)\right]$$

$$18.5 = \frac{100}{110}\left(V_{\mathrm{IN}} + 13.5\right)$$

$$V_{\mathrm{IN}} = 6.85\,\mathrm{V}$$

Therefore V_{IN} must rise to +6.85 V to switch V_{OUT} from −13.5 to +13.5 V. The value 6.85 V is the upper trigger point (UTP) for this circuit. V_{OUT} will remain at +13.5 V when V_{IN} falls below +6.85 V because of the positive feedback causing an increase in the voltage at V_2.

Using potential divider theory (see Fig 9.27(b)), the value of V_{IN} needed to switch the output from +13.5 V to −13.5 V is calculated as 4.15 V.

Fig 9.27   Non-inverting Schmitt trigger circuit considered as a potential divider to determine (a) the upper trigger point and (b) the lower trigger point.

Therefore V_{IN} must fall to 4.15 V to switch V_{OUT} from +13.5 V to −13.5 V. The value 4.15 V is the **lower trigger point (LTP)** for this circuit.

As the LDR is illuminated, the output switches to a high state when V_{IN} rises to +6.85 V. When the LDR is darkened, the output switches low when V_{IN} falls to 4.15 V. The switching points are summarised by the graph in Fig 9.28. The difference between the switching levels is called the **hysteresis**.

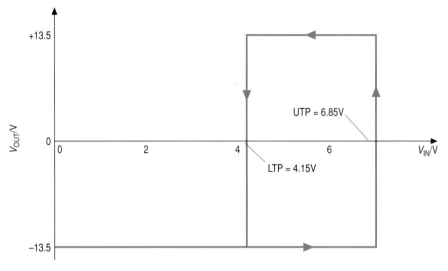

Fig 9.28   Hysteresis for a Schmitt trigger.

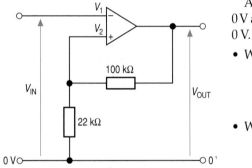

Fig 9.29   Symmetrical Schmitt trigger.

A **symmetrical Schmitt trigger** is shown in Fig 9.29. If R_{IN} is connected to 0 V as shown in Fig 9.29, then the two trigger points will be symmetrical about 0 V. A simple calculation will demonstrate this:

- When V_{OUT} = +13.5 V then

$$V_2 = \frac{22}{122} \times 13.5 = +2.43\,V$$

- When V_{OUT} = −13.5 V then

$$V_2 = \frac{22}{122} \times (-13.5) = -2.43\,V$$

If the two resistors are equal the UTP and LTP are symmetrical about 0 V and are equal to half the saturated output voltage, i.e. ±6.75 V for a ±15 V supply.

Oscillator

An inverting Schmitt trigger can be converted to a free-running (relaxation) **oscillator** as shown in Fig 9.30.

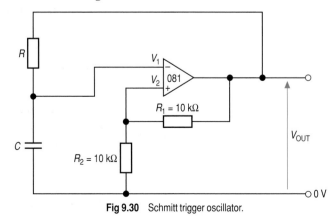

Fig 9.30   Schmitt trigger oscillator.

THE OPERATIONAL AMPLIFIER

The output voltage changes continuously between the positive and negative saturation voltages as the capacitor alternately charges and discharges through R. The output switches to –13.5 V when V_1 rises above the UTP and switches to +13.5 V when V_1 falls below the LTP (–13.5 V and +13.5 V are the saturation output voltages for the 081 op-amp). If R_1 and R_2 are equal, then the LTP = –6.75 V and the UTP = +6.75 V (these values can be calculated using potential divider theory). The output is approximately a square wave and the following equation gives the period T of the square wave:

$$T = 2.2CR$$

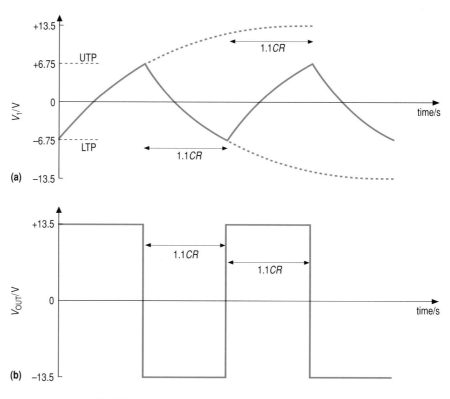

Fig 9.31 **(a)** Input and **(b)** output waveforms for oscillator circuit.

The graphs in Fig 9.31 illustrate the switching characteristics of the circuit when $R_1 = R_2$. If the resistors R_1 and R_2 are not equal, the period can be calculated from:

$$T = 2CR \ln\left(1 + 2\frac{R_2}{R_1}\right)$$

The derivation of this equation is given in the box below.

The charging equation is given by

$$V = V_0(1 - e^{-t/CR}) \tag{1}$$

and LTP = V_x and UTP= V_y.

The proof is not as complex as it looks. It is cumbersome because the charging voltage starts from a negative value, not zero (see Fig 9.31), which must be taken into account when using equation (1). Therefore, in equation (1),

$$V_0 = V_{sat} - V_x \qquad \text{and} \qquad V = V_y - V_x$$

If it takes t seconds for the capacitor to charge up from the LTP V_x to the UTP V_y then substituting these values into eqation (1) gives

$$V_y - V_x = (V_{sat} - V_x)(1 - e^{-t/CR}) \qquad (2)$$

Using potential divider theory,

$$V_x = -\frac{R_2}{R_1 + R_2} V_{sat} \qquad \text{and} \qquad V_y = +\frac{R_2}{R_1 + R_2} V_{sat}$$

Substituting these values into equation (2) gives

$$\frac{R_2}{R_1 + R_2} V_{sat} - \left(-\frac{R_2}{R_1 + R_2} V_{sat}\right) = \left[V_{sat} - \left(-\frac{R_2}{R_1 + R_2} V_{sat}\right)\right]\left(1 - e^{-t/CR}\right)$$

$$\frac{2R_2}{R_1 + R_2} V_{sat} = V_{sat}\left(1 + \frac{R_2}{R_1 + R_2}\right)\left(1 - e^{-t/CR}\right)$$

$$\frac{2R_2}{R_1 + R_2} = \left(\frac{R_1 + R_2 + R_2}{R_1 + R_2}\right)\left(1 - e^{-t/CR}\right)$$

$$2R_2 = \left(R_1 + 2R_2\right)\left(1 - e^{-t/CR}\right)$$

$$\frac{2R_2}{R_1 + 2R_2} = \left(1 - e^{-t/CR}\right)$$

$$1 - \frac{2R_2}{R_1 + 2R_2} = e^{-t/CR}$$

$$\frac{R_1}{R_1 + 2R_2} = e^{-t/CR}$$

Taking natural logarithms of both sides of the equation:

$$\ln\left(\frac{R_1}{R_1 + 2R_2}\right) = -\frac{t}{CR}$$

$$\ln\left(\frac{R_1 + 2R_2}{R_1}\right) = \frac{t}{CR}$$

Therefore

$$t = CR\ln\left(1 + \frac{2R_2}{R_1}\right)$$

The time for the capacitor to discharge from V_y to V_x is also t seconds. So finally the period is

$$T = 2CR\ln\left(1 + \frac{2R_2}{R_1}\right)$$

QUESTION

9.5 Calculate the frequency of oscillation of the Schmitt trigger oscillator circuit in Fig 9.30 if $C = 100\,\text{nF}$, $R = 10\,\text{k}\Omega$, $R_1 = 100\,\text{k}\Omega$ and $R_2 = 47\,\text{k}\Omega$.

SUMMARY

$$V_{OUT} = A_{OL}(V_2 - V_1)$$

Negative feedback is used in amplifying circuits to reduce the gain.

THE OPERATIONAL AMPLIFIER

For the inverting amplifier (Fig 9.32)

$$A_{CL} = -\frac{R_F}{R_{IN}}$$

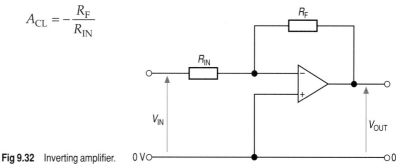

Fig 9.32 Inverting amplifier.

For the non-inverting amplifier (Fig 9.33)

$$A_{CL} = 1 + \frac{R_F}{R_{IN}}$$

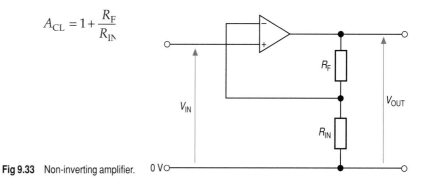

Fig 9.33 Non-inverting amplifier.

A voltage follower is a non-inverting amplifier with a gain of 1.

Uses of an op-amp: buffer amplifier, coloumbmeter, nanoammeter.

Difference amplifier – amplifies the difference between the two input signals.

Summing amplifier – the output voltage is equal to the algebraic sum of the two input voltages.

Ramp generator – the output voltage increases linearly for the length of time that there is a difference between the two inputs.

Comparator – compares the two input voltages and gives a digital output state depending on which input is larger.

Positive feedback is used in Schmitt trigger and oscillator circuits.

Schmitt trigger – the output changes state when the input rises above the UTP and remains in that state until the input falls below the LTP.

Theme 4

MICROPROCESSOR SYSTEMS

The modern world of high technology would not have arisen without the development of the computer. Different types and sizes of computers find uses throughout society in the storage and handling of data. Computers have opened up a new era in manufacturing through automation techniques, and they have enhanced modern communication systems.

Any digital system uses only two signal levels, 'high' or 'low', which in logical terms is 'true' or 'false' or numerically '1' or '0' respectively. All information is presented to a computer as electrical signals in a large variety of forms, analogue, digital coded, different frequencies, etc., and they all need to be converted to a binary representation which the computer can use. Similarly binary outputs from the computer must be converted to suitable signals which the output devices can recognise. Data in analogue form can be fed into a digital computer by means of an analogue-to-digital converter, and the same is true of the reverse situation with the use of a digital-to-analogue converter.

An inventor plays a duet with his robotic creation, Wabot-2, at the Tokyo Exposition. Building this kind of robot is a challenging task because the dexterity of the human hand is perhaps the most difficult function to re-create mechanically. Although Wabot-2's performance may not be emotional, with an electronic scanning eye and quality components, the technical accuracy will be extremely high.

Chapter 10

DATA CONVERTER SYSTEMS

LEARNING OBJECTIVES

After studying this chapter you should be able to:

1. understand the principles of analogue-to-digital and digital-to analogue conversion;

2. draw block diagrams of different types of analogue-to-digital converter;

3. understand the use of the weighted resistor and the $R–2R$ networks for digital-to-analogue conversion.

10.1 ANALOGUE-TO-DIGITAL CONVERSION

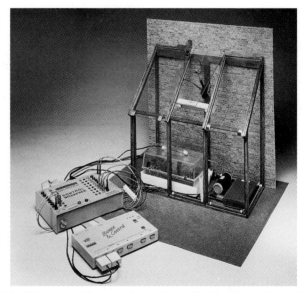

Fig 10.1 This computer is being used to monitor conditions inside a model greenhouse.

Digital systems use the binary system of counting; signals are either on or off. The real world is composed of continually varying signals; for example, the output voltage from a light-sensing potential divider unit is not simply on or off since the light falling on the sensor is not simply light or dark. The photograph in Fig 10.1 shows a computer being used to monitor the environment inside a model greenhouse. The input sensors consist of a light sensor and temperature sensor both producing analogue signals. In order for the computer to respond to the changes produced by the sensors, the analogue signals must be converted into digital signals. The process block required is an **analogue-to-digital (A/D) converter** or **ADC**. If the analogue voltage ranges from 0 to 2.55 V and is converted to a digital output (binary code) by means of an eight-bit ADC, which gives the range 0000 0000 to 1111 1111, a change of one bit represents a change of 0.01 V. Therefore an input voltage of 1.20 V will be converted into a digital output of 0111 1000.

Fig 10.2 A multimeter can be used as a digital voltmeter (DVM).

Three types of ADC will be considered: the **counter/ramp,** the **flash converter** and the **successive approximation** ADC.

Counter and ramp ADC

This type of ADC is used in **digital voltmeters (DVM)** like the one shown in Fig 10.2. The basic block diagram of a DVM is drawn in Fig 10.3.

The output from the ramp generator and the analogue voltage being measured are both fed into a comparator. When the analogue input voltage is greater than the ramp voltage, the output voltage from the comparator goes high since V_2 is then greater than V_1. When the ramp voltage becomes larger than the measured voltage, the comparator switches the AND gate output to logic 0, which stops the count. The timing diagrams in Fig 10.4 explain the operation of the DVM. For an input voltage of 3 V the counter counts three clock pulses before it resets. The digital output from the counter is proportional to the analogue input voltage.

This type of ADC is fairly accurate but is very slow, taking about 1 second to complete a conversion. The fastest type of converter is known as a flash converter which uses several comparators and some decoding logic circuits to produce a digital output.

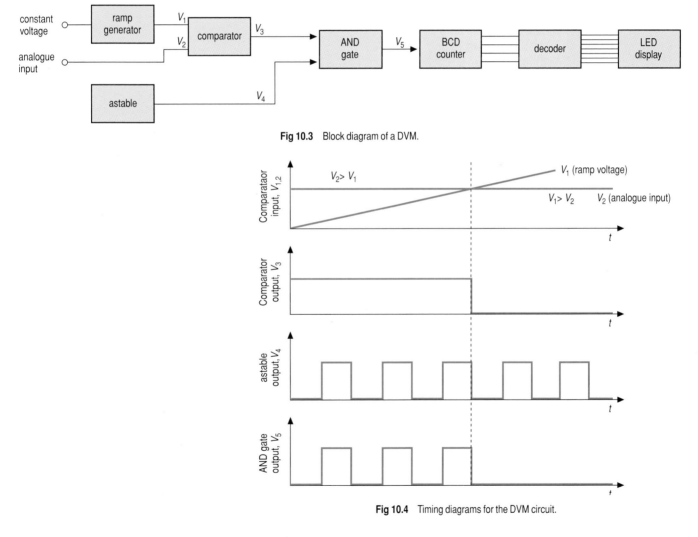

Fig 10.3 Block diagram of a DVM.

Fig 10.4 Timing diagrams for the DVM circuit.

Flash converter

A simple flash ADC is shown in Fig 10.5. A chain or 'ladder' of $10\,k\Omega$ resistors is used to produce different reference voltages for each comparator. The truth table in Table 10.1 explains how the circuit operates.

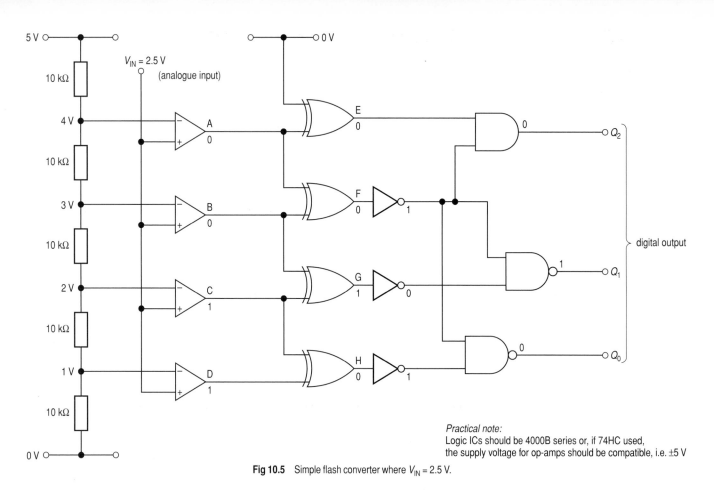

Fig 10.5   Simple flash converter where $V_{IN} = 2.5$ V.

Practical note:
Logic ICs should be 4000B series or, if 74HC used,
the supply voltage for op-amps should be compatible, i.e. ±5 V

Table 10.1   **Truth table for flash converter ADC**

V_{IN}/V		A	B	C	D	E = $A \oplus 0$	F = $A \oplus B$	G = $B \oplus C$	H = $C \oplus D$	$Q_2 = E.\bar{F}$	$Q_1 = \overline{\overline{F.G}}$	$Q_0 = \overline{\overline{F.H}}$
(0–1)	0.5	0	0	0	0	0	0	0	0	0	0	0
(1–2)	1.5	0	0	0	1	0	0	0	1	0	0	1
(2–3)	2.5	0	0	1	1	0	0	1	0	0	1	0
(3–4)	3.5	0	1	1	1	0	1	0	0	0	1	1
(4–5)	4.5	1	1	1	1	1	0	0	0	1	0	0

To calculate the resolution for a chain of eight 10 kΩ resistors used with seven comparators in a circuit similar to Fig 10.5 a change of 1 bit would result in a change of 5 V/8 = 0.625 V. The resolution of the circuit

$$= \frac{0.625}{5} \times 100 \approx 13\%$$

When the analogue input is 2.5 V as in Fig 10.5, the comparator outputs at C and D are at logic 1 since the input voltage is greater than their reference voltages. An EX-OR gate gives a logic 1 output only when its inputs are different, so point G will be at logic 1. Note that the gate preceding Q_2 is an AND gate. The logic signals for an input voltage of 2.5 V are shown in Fig 10.5.

The problem with the circuit in Fig 10.5 is its lack of **resolution**, which is only 20%, i.e. a change of one bit represents a change of 1.0 V. To use the **full range** (where all possible binary codes are present) of the three-bit output in Fig 10.5, i.e. for an input of 5 V to represent the binary output 111, seven comparators would be needed and the resolution would be 13%. An ADC is said to have a **useful resolution** of n bits when no missing codes are present. It is usual to specify the resolution of an ADC as 'eight bits', 'twelve bits', etc. To improve the resolution, more comparators are needed and 256 identical resistors, which means that this method of analogue-to-digital conversion is quite expensive. Conversion speeds are fast (typically 50 ns) because all the bits of the output are determined at the same time.

A less expensive type of ADC is the **successive approximation** type, which is slower than the flash converter but much faster than the counter and ramp type.

DATA CONVERTER SYSTEMS

Successive approximation ADC

A block diagram of a four-bit successive approximation converter is shown in Fig 10.6.

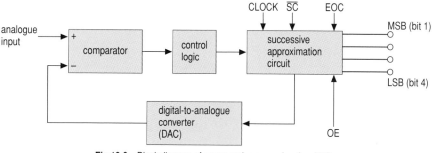

Fig 10.6 Block diagram of a successive approximation ADC.

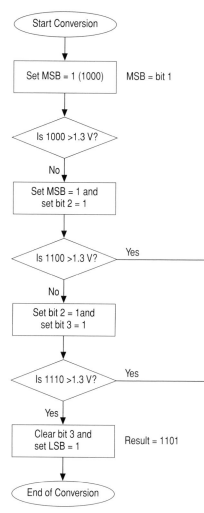

Fig 10.7 Flowchart to explain the operation of the successive approximation converter.

The conversion is initiated by supplying the **start conversion** ($\overline{SC}$) input with a negative-edge clock pulse (hence the bar over the symbol). The most-significant bit (MSB) is then set to logic 1 and all the other bits are set to logic 0. This digital output 1000 is converted to an analogue voltage (say 0.8 V) by the **digital-to-analogue converter (DAC)** (section 10.2). The comparator compares this voltage with the analogue input voltage and a decision is then made on the next negative-edge clock pulse either to reset the MSB to 0 or to leave it set at 1 depending on the size of the voltage compared with the size of the analogue input voltage. The next MSB is set to 1 on the same clock pulse and the new output voltage from the DAC is again compared with the size of the analogue input voltage and a decision is made with reference to this second MSB. This process is repeated for all four bits, and on the fifth negative-edge clock pulse the **end of conversion** (EOC) goes high, indicating that the conversion is complete. The procedure of a successive approximation converter to convert 1.3 V into the digital output equivalent of 1101 is summed up in the flowchart of Fig 10.7. The ZN427 IC is an example of an eight-bit successive approximation ADC.

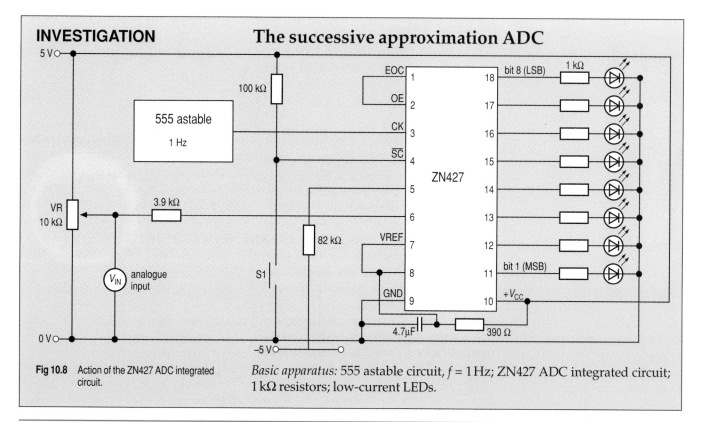

Fig 10.8 Action of the ZN427 ADC integrated circuit.

Basic apparatus: 555 astable circuit, $f = 1\,\text{Hz}$; ZN427 ADC integrated circuit; 1 kΩ resistors; low-current LEDs.

Set up the circuit in Fig 10.8 on a breadboard. The control pins are labelled as: pin 4 = start conversion, $\overline{SC}$; pin 2 = output enable, OE; pin 1 = end of conversion, EOC.

Note: There are eight bits, which means that the conversion will be complete on the ninth clock pulse. The use of the slow astable will enable you to count the pulses once the conversion begins. The reference voltage for this IC is 2.56 V, which means that the full range of binary codes is 00000000 to 11111111 (equivalent to 0.00 to 2.55 V).

Using the potential divider VR, set V_{IN} to about 0.5 V. Start the conversion by connecting pin 4 momentarily low by pressing and then releasing switch S1. After nine pulses the binary output will be displayed by means of the LEDs. Increase V_{IN} in equal steps until $V_{IN} = 2.5$ V and repeat the procedure. Record your observations in a table like Table 10.2.

Table 10.2   Results of the investigation

Analogue input	Digital output							
V_{IN}/V	Bit 1 MSB	Bit 2	Bit 3	Bit 4	Bit 5	Bit 6	Bit 7	Bit 8 LSB
0.50	0	0	1	1	0	0	1	0
etc.	etc.							

IC pin notations
You may find alternative abbreviations used for the control pins of analogue-to-digital ICs:

$\overline{WR}$ = write$\left(\overline{SC}\right)$
RD = read (OE)
BUSY (EOC)

In practical applications, the output enable (OE) pin is normally held low and the output data can only be read if OE is taken high at the end of the conversion. If, as in the previous investigation, EOC is tied to OE then the output will be enabled automatically at the end of the conversion.

The clock frequency and the resolution of an ADC determine the **conversion time**. If the clock frequency for an n-bit successive approximation ADC is f Hz, the conversion time, in seconds, is given by:

$$\text{conversion time} = \frac{n+1}{f}$$

The '$n + 1$' is needed because the first pulse initialises the system and clears the DAC to zero.

Example: For a 900 kHz clock frequency the conversion time for an eight-bit successive approximation ADC is given by:

$$\text{conversion time} = \frac{8+1}{900 \times 10^3} = 10^{-5}\,\text{s} = 10\,\mu\text{s}$$

In the previous investigation, the conversion time was deliberately made long (9 s) to enable you to 'see' what was happening. This did not present any problems regarding the **accuracy** of conversion since the signals converted at any one time were not changing. However, if the analogue signal is continually changing, it is important that the conversion time is as short as possible. This itself can create problems since, to increase the resolution, the number of bits must increase which will increase the conversion time.

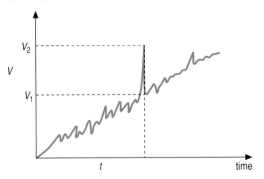

Fig 10.9   The effect of noise on conversions.

DATA CONVERTER SYSTEMS

If the analogue voltage is continually changing, the conversion time or 'sampling period' must be less than the time it takes for the signal to change its value significantly. The faster the **sampling rate** (determined by the clock period and the number of bits), the better the digital representation. Noise can also create errors in conversion as shown in Fig 10.9. At time t, the actual sample voltage is V_1, but due to noise the measured value is V_2.

Sample-and-hold circuits

To ensure that the analogue signal being sampled is kept steady during the successive approximation process, a **sample-and-hold** circuit is often used on the input of the ADC. Consider the changing analogue voltage in Fig 10.10. If the analogue-to-digital conversion begins at time t_1 when the voltage is 1.00 V and the conversion ends at time t_2, then the digital output will be 1100 1000 (2.00 V) instead of 0110 0100 (1.00 V) where the LSB is 0.01 V.

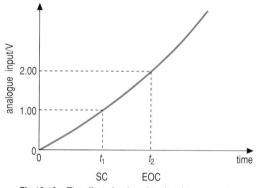

Fig 10.10   The effect of a changing signal on conversions.

A system is needed that will hold the analogue input at 1.00 V until the conversion is complete. A simple sample-and-hold circuit is shown in Fig 10.11. It consists of a switch, a capacitor and a voltage follower. When the switch is opened the capacitor holds the value of the input voltage at that instant. The op-amp has a high input resistance, which prevents the capacitor discharging during the time the switch is open.

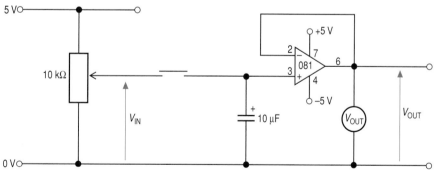

Fig 10.11   A sample-and-hold circuit.

10.2 DIGITAL-TO-ANALOGUE CONVERSION

So far, only analogue-to-digital conversion has been considered. The computer in Fig 10.1 is being used to control the environment in the model greenhouse. The digital output from the computer is being used to switch the motor of the **ram-rod** (Fig 10.12) on and off to open and close the window. If the computer is being used to operate an output device which requires an analogue action, such as varying the speed of the motor, then a process block is needed which will convert the digital output to an analogue output. The process block is called a **digital-to-analogue (D/A) converter** or **DAC**.

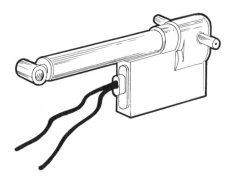

Fig 10.12 A ram-rod.

As with ADCs, ICs are readily available which convert digital to analogue signals. Some of the principles of conversion will be considered before investigating the types of IC available.

The use of a summing amplifier in digital-to-analogue conversion

Fig 10.13 shows how a summing amplifier can be used with a series of **'weighted'** resistors, i.e. R, $2R$, $4R$, $8R$, etc., to convert a four-bit digital code into its analogue equivalent.

Point P is the virtual earth point. Therefore

$$V_{OUT} = -IR_F$$
$$= -R_F(I_1 + I_2 + I_3 + I_4)$$
$$= -R_F\left(\frac{V_1}{R} + \frac{V_2}{2R} + \frac{V_3}{4R} + \frac{V_4}{8R}\right)$$

A four-bit binary word is applied to the DAC by means of four switches which can be connected either to the 5 V reference voltage, if the input bit is at logic 1, or to 0 V, if the input voltage is at logic 0. The switches are connected to the summing amplifier via a weighted resistor network.

For the switch connections shown in Fig 10.13, the binary input code is 1100. If $R = 10\,k\Omega$ and $R_F = 1\,k\Omega$ then

$$V_{OUT} = -\left(\frac{5}{10} + \frac{5}{20} + \frac{0}{40} + \frac{0}{80}\right) = -0.75\,V$$

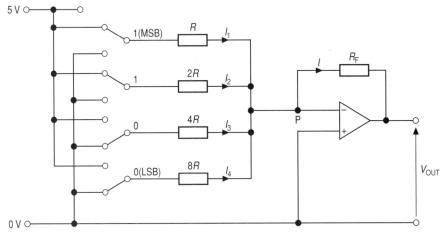

Fig 10.13 Summing amplifier with weighted resistor network.

QUESTIONS

10.1 In Fig 10.13 R_F is replaced with a 3.3 kΩ resistor. Calculate the analogue output voltage when the binary input code is 1100.

10.2 If $R = 10\,k\Omega$ and $R_F = 1\,k\Omega$ in Fig 10.13 then calculate the equivalent analogue output voltage for each binary input code. Record your answers in a table like Table 10.3.

Table 10.3   Answer to question 10.2

Binary input code				Analogue output/V
0	0	0	0	0.0000
0	0	0	1	−0.0625
0	0	1	0	
etc.				
1	1	1	1	

DATA CONVERTER SYSTEMS

For the circuit drawn in Fig 10.13, a change of one bit in the binary information is equivalent to a change of 0.0625 V. If there are eight bit inputs to the DAC above then

$$V_{OUT} = -R_F\left(\frac{V_1}{R} + \frac{V_2}{2R} + \frac{V_3}{4R} + \frac{V_4}{8R} + \frac{V_5}{16R} + \frac{V_6}{32R} + \frac{V_7}{64R} + \frac{V_8}{128R}\right)$$

The smallest step in the output voltage (LSB) is now 0.0039 V; this is called the **resolution**. Higher resolution requires a larger number of input bits.

The problem with this weighted resistor DAC is that the range of resistor values needed for high resolution is large. To achieve accuracy in the conversion, resistors must have a very low tolerance and their values must vary by the same amount with temperature.

To overcome the problem of requiring a large range of resistor values, an **R–2R network** is used as shown in Fig 10.14.

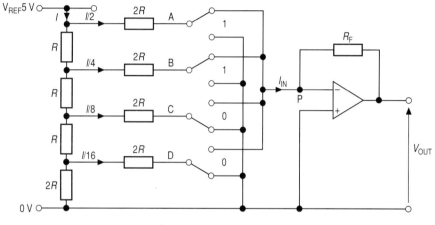

Fig 10.14   An R—2R network.

Points A, B, C and D of the R–2R network in Fig 10.14 can be connected either to the virtual earth of the op-amp when the input to the amplifier is a '1' or to 0 V when the input is a '0'.

It can be shown that the total resistance of the R–2R network is equal to R and therefore

$$I = \frac{V_{REF}}{R}$$

When points A, B, C and D in Fig 10.14 are connected to point P then

$$I_{IN} = \frac{I}{2} + \frac{I}{4} + \frac{I}{8} + \frac{I}{16}$$

The analogue output voltage can be calculated using the formula $V_{OUT} = -I_{IN}R_F$ where I_{IN} is the input current to the op-amp from the R–2R network and R_F is the feedback resistance. I_{IN} depends on the switch connections representing the digital input.

Example: What is the analogue output for a binary input code of 1100 applied to the circuit in Fig 10.14 if the reference voltage is 5 V, $R = 10\,k\Omega$ and $R_F = 3.3\,k\Omega$?
We have

$$I = \frac{5\,V}{10\,k\Omega} = 0.5\,mA$$

$$I_{IN} = \frac{I}{2} + \frac{I}{4} = \frac{0.5}{2} + \frac{0.5}{4} = 0.375\,mA$$

$$V_{OUT} = -0.375\,mA \times 3.3\,k\Omega = -1.24\,V$$

10.3 Using the data given in the example above, calculate V_{OUT} when the binary input code is **(a)** 0001 and **(b)** 1111.

This R–$2R$ circuit is superior to the weighted DAC because the only resistor values needed are R and $2R$ independent of the number of bits. These can be easily manufactured on an IC so that the resistors have identical properties.

INVESTIGATION

The R–$2R$ network

Construct the R–$2R$ DAC in Fig 10.15.

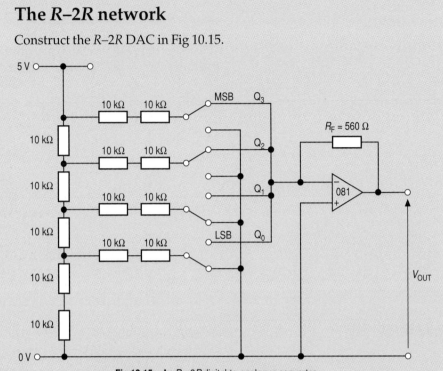

Fig 10.15 An R—$2R$ digital-to-analogue converter.

Draw up a truth table as in Table 10.4 and measure the analogue output voltage V_{OUT} for the full range of possible binary inputs from 0000 to 1111. Repeat the procedure with $R_F = 10\,k\Omega$.

Table 10.4 Results of the investigation

Q_3	Q_2	Q_1	Q_0	V_{OUT}/V
0	0	0	0	
0	0	0	1	
0	0	1	0	

etc.

Available DACs

The ZN428 IC in Fig 10.16 is an eight-bit DAC which uses the R–$2R$ ladder technique. It contains eight input latches to facilitate updating information from a data bus in computer applications (see Chapter 11).

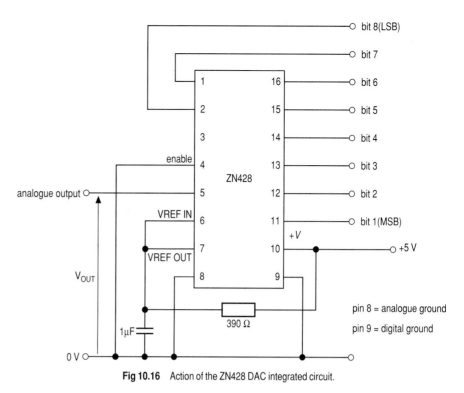

Fig 10.16 Action of the ZN428 DAC integrated circuit.

The latch is said to be transparent when enable is low, which means that the output voltage is lost when the binary input is disconnected. The data is held, i.e. changes in the input do not affect the output, when enable is taken high. The binary input 1111 1111 ≡ 2.55 V.

SUMMARY

An analogue-to-digital converter converts an analogue input into a digital output with a weight that relates to the size of the analogue input.

A four-bit ADC has a useful resolution of four bits if there are no missing binary codes at the digital output.

The conversion time is the time it takes to convert an analogue to a digital signal.

Three common circuits for analogue-to-digital functions are the counter and ramp, flash converter and successive approximation.

A sample-and-hold circuit is used with an ADC to keep the analogue voltage steady during the conversion.

A digital-to-analogue converter converts a digital input into an analogue output.

A summing amplifier is used with weighted resistor or R–$2R$ networks to construct a DAC.

R–$2R$ networks are preferred to weighted resistors because they only use two resistor values.

Chapter  11

COMPUTER SYSTEMS

LEARNING OBJECTIVES

After studying this chapter you should be able to:

1. use the hexadecimal code;

2. recall the essential subsystems of a computer;

3. recall the function of the bus lines;

4. give examples of input and output peripherals;

5. understand the function of a shift register;

6. describe the different types of memory in a computer system.

11.1 DATA REPRESENTATION

All data used by computers is code. Different computers use different codes and different parts of the same computer use different codes. The common factor is that the codes are based on the binary system, which uses only two numbers, 0 and 1. Often it is necessary to store and transmit alphabetic data in digital form such as for storing text within a computer. The widely used **ASCII code** is a character code in which each alphabetic character is coded separately as a set of seven binary digits.

Considerable attention is given to the detection and correction of errors in the design of computers. When coded information is transmitted, errors can arise through interference causing one bit to be lost which makes nonsense of the information being received. The simplest self-checking code requires the inclusion of a **parity bit** as the eighth bit of the ASCII code. At the receiving end, an error-checking device counts the number of '1's in each received code. If 'even parity checking' is used it expects to receive an even number of '1's and 'odd parity checking' expects an odd number of '1's. At the transmitting end, a '1' or a '0' is included as the eighth bit to make the total number of digits even or odd depending on which mode of checking is used. The ASCII character for 'B' is 100 0001 which has an even number of '1's. Therefore in even parity checking, a 0 parity is added to make an eight-bit code which still has an even number of '1's. The transmitted code is now *0*100 0001. (Note that here the parity bit is in *italics*.)

Binary-coded-decimal (BCD) is a popular way of representing numbers within a computer. In binary-coded decimal, each digit of a decimal number is converted into its binary equivalent.

Example: Decimal 59 becomes 0101 1001 in BCD.

There are obvious disadvantages for users who are programming and interpreting computer data in binary code. This is because the binary numbers can consist of many bits; even a reasonably small decimal number (say 59) becomes a cumbersome six-bit binary word (111011). In order to make the binary system more user-friendly, several systems have been devised to make the numbers more recognisable. These include **hexadecimal**, numbers to the

ASCII
ASCII stands for American Standard Code for Information Interchange.

base 16, and **octal**, numbers to the base 8, which have the advantage of being concise and can be easily converted to binary.

In **hexadecimal** the decimal numbers 10, 11, 12, 13, 14 and 15 are represented by the letters A, B, C, D, E and F. On liquid-crystal or seven-segment displays lower-case letters b and d are used for B and D because B may be confused with 8 and D with 0 when displayed.

Example: Converting hexadecimal numbers into decimal numbers.

$$\text{hexadecimal } 10 = (1 \times 16^1) + (0 \times 16^0)$$
$$= 16$$
$$\text{hexadecimal DA} = (13 \times 16^1) + (10 \times 16^0)$$
$$= 218$$
$$\text{hexadecimal F3} = (15 \times 16^1) + (3 \times 16^0)$$
$$= 243$$

Example: Converting the decimal number 1023 into hexadecimal.

$$1023 \div 16 = 63 \text{ remainder } \quad F$$
$$63 \div 16 = 3 \text{ remainder } F$$
$$3 \div 16 = 0 \text{ remainder } 3$$
$$1023 \text{ (decimal)} = 3 \text{ FF (hexadecimal)}$$

QUESTIONS

11.1 Convert the following hexadecimal numbers into decimal numbers: **(a)** FF, **(b)** 4B, **(c)** 5CA, **(d)** E3A.

11.2 Convert the following decimal numbers into hexadecimal numbers: **(a)** 17, **(b)** 90, **(c)** 239, **(d)** 3338.

Octal numbers are derived by similar methods.

Example: Converting octal numbers into decimal numbers.

$$\text{octal } 332 = (3 \times 8^2) + (3 \times 8^1) + (2 \times 8^0)$$
$$= 218$$

Example: Converting decimal numbers into octal.

$$31 \div 8 = 3 \text{ remainder } \quad 7$$
$$3 \div 8 = 0 \text{ remainder } 3$$
$$31 \text{ (decimal)} = 37 \text{ (octal)}$$

Many computers use binary numbers processed in groups of four or eight bits, so it is convenient to use the hexadecimal equivalent of the binary number. To express a binary number in hexadecimal, the binary bits are arranged in groups of four, called **nibbles**, starting from the right, and the hexadecimal value is given for each nibble. A binary **word** refers to a string of bits that stores a unit of information in a computer. A binary word usually represents four bytes. A nibble contains four bits and a byte contains eight bits or two nibbles.

Example: Converting binary words into hexadecimal.

0011	0111		binary word
3	7		hexadecimal
0110	1100		binary word
6	C		hexadecimal
0010	1110	0111	binary word
2	E	7	hexadecimal

11.3 Convert the following binary numbers into hexadecimal numbers: **(a)** 0010 1111, **(b)** 0011 0110, **(c)** 1010 1011, **(d)** 1111 1111.

11.4 Convert the following hexadecimal numbers into binary numbers: **(a)** FE, **(b)** 4B, **(c)** 5CA, **(d)** E3A.

To express a binary number in octal, the binary bits are arranged in groups of three, starting from the least significant end, and the octal value is given for each group.

Example: Converting binary words into octal.

| 110 | 111 | | binary word |
| 6 | 7 | | octal |

| 001 | 101 | 100 | binary word |
| 1 | 5 | 4 | octal |

A comparison of the various codes is given in Table 11.1.

Table 11.1   A comparison of the various codes

Decimal	Binary	BCD	Octal	HEX	ASCII code	ASCII character
0	0000 0000	0000 0000	00	00	011 0000	0
1	0000 0001	0000 0001	01	01	011 0001	1
2	0000 0010	0000 0010	02	02	011 0010	2
3	0000 0011	0000 0011	03	03	011 0011	3
4	0000 0100	0000 0100	04	04	011 0100	4
5	0000 0101	0000 0101	05	05	011 0101	5
6	0000 0110	0000 0110	06	06	011 0110	6
7	0000 0111	0000 0111	07	07	011 0111	7
8	0000 1000	0000 1000	10	08	011 1000	8
9	0000 1001	0000 1001	11	09	011 1001	9
10	0000 1010	0001 0000	12	0A	011 1010	:
11	0000 1011	0001 0001	13	0B	011 1011	;
12	0000 1100	0001 0010	14	0C	011 1100	<
13	0000 1101	0001 0011	15	0D	011 1101	=
14	0000 1110	0001 0100	16	0E	011 1110	>
15	0000 1111	0001 0101	17	0F	011 1111	?
16	0001 0000	0001 0110	20	10	100 0000	@

The various number codes discussed so far use **unsigned** binary numbers. On some applications it is important to represent not only the magnitude of a quantity but also its **polarity**. One way of doing this is to use the most significant bit of an n-bit number to represent the **sign bit**. A positive number is represented by a sign bit of '0' and a negative number with a sign bit of '1'. However most computers use an alternative method called the **two's complement** system. To obtain the two's complement of a positive number, invert all the bits of the positive number and add '1' to the LSB of the inverted number.

Example:

$$+3 = 0000\ 0011$$
$$-3 = 1111\ 1100$$
$$+1$$
$$= 1111\ 1101$$

The procedure provides a simple method for a computer to subtract one number from another by obtaining the two's complement of the number to be subtracted and adding it to the other number.

11.2 COMPUTER SYSTEM

Like any other system a **computer system** can be broken down into subsystems to enable us to understand the function of it more easily. The basic block diagram of a computer system is shown in Fig 11.1. The external peripheral devices are not shown; they will be considered independently.

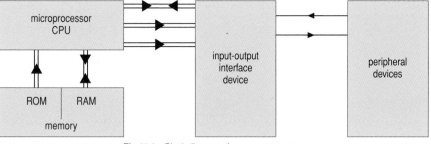

Fig 11.1 Block diagram of a computer system.

The subsystems shown in Fig 11.1 can consist of either single ICs such as the microprocessor or several ICs as in the memory subsystem.

At the 'heart' of the computer is the **microprocessor** or **central processing unit (CPU)** which requires a memory in which to store the operating program. Input peripherals, such as a keyboard and mouse, and output peripherals, such as a monitor and printer, cannot be connected directly to the CPU as the data between the two is incompatible. Therefore, input and output interface circuits are required. The speed with which the computer can move data between the various subsystems needs to be very fast, and this is achieved by sending data along several wires grouped in parallel to transfer several bits of data simultaneously. Theses groups of wires are called **buses**.

11.3 THE BUS SYSTEM

There are three buses: the data, address and control buses. The number of wires in each bus depends on the particular microprocessor being used.

The **data bus** is used to send information and instructions *from* the CPU *to* the memory or peripherals. Data can also be sent *to* the CPU *from* the memory or peripherals as shown by the bidirectional arrows on Fig 11.2. Personal computers started with eight-bit data buses but now the faster systems contain 16-bit and 32-bit buses.

The CPU has to determine which IC or peripheral the data is to be written to or read from. It does this by allocating a unique address for each piece of data it writes or reads. In the case of a 16-line **address bus** the address will consist of a two-byte number. The more address bus lines there are, the more memory the CPU can address. For a computer with 16 address lines the total number of memory locations is 2^{16} (65 536), known as 64K ('1K' in binary terms is actually 1024 bytes). Usually the address bus operates in one direction, that is, data is transferred from the CPU.

The **control bus** carries the control instructions (which may be simply 'read' or 'write') from the CPU to the rest of the system.

The data bus is **bidirectional**, which means that information is sent and received along the same line. **Tristate buffer** devices are used to enable the data to be either read from or written to this common data bus.

A tristate is a logic gate which has three output states. There are two types of tristate logic gate, one with an active high control, the other with active low control. The symbols and truth tables are shown in Fig 11.3.

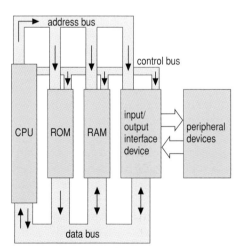

Fig 11.2 Block diagram of bus connections.

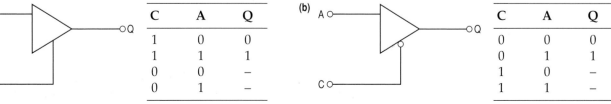

Fig 11.3 The tristate: **(a)** active high control; **(b)** active low control.

For the active high control tristate, if the control input C = 1 then the output state Q is the same as that of the input A, the two possible output states being 0 or 1. If C = 0 then a third output state is possible in which the output can 'float' up and down freely and is effectively disconnected from the input A. Fig 11.4 shows an eight-bit latch connected to the eight lines of the data bus. The latch outputs are connected to the control inputs of active high control tristate buffers. The control inputs are connected to, and therefore controlled by, the read line on the control bus. The clock of the D-type latch is connected to the write line. When write switches from logic 0 to logic 1 (positive-edge triggered) the data input of each flip-flop (D_0 to D_7) is written to and stored on its output terminal. If the read signal is at logic 1 the output of each flip-flop (Q_0 to Q_7) is fed out to the eight lines of the data bus. When the read input is at logic 0 the output of the tristate is turned off and does not interfere with the data already on the data bus. In this way the data can be read from the data bus.

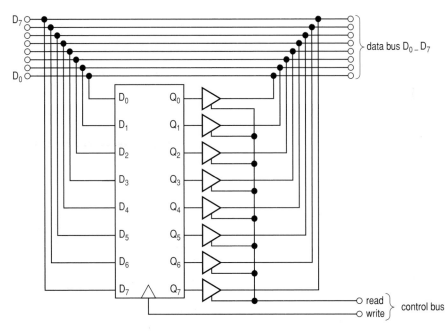

Fig 11.4   Data bus connections to an eight-bit latch.

11.4 PROGRAMS

For a computer to operate it has to be **programmed** with a sequential list of instructions and data which represent the task to be performed. **Machine code** is the basic language understood by microprocessors. It consists of byte instructions followed by data or address locations. It is not easy to understand machine code as it simply appears as a list of hexadecimal numbers. **High-level languages** such as BASIC, Pascal and 'C' are easier to understand because they use English to describe the operations. A computer cannot directly run a program written in a high-level language; it must first be translated to machine code by a program called a **compiler**. An improvement on machine code is **assembler language** which uses abbreviations of the instruction codes, called **mnemonics**, and HEX numbers for data and addresses. A conversion program called **Assembler** is used to produce the machine code. All microprocessors have an instruction set of mnemonics which are different, although similar, for each manufacturer's devices.

Table 11.2 illustrates some of the mnemonics and machine code instructions for the 6502 microprocessor.

A useful kit for learning how to program using machine code is the '3-Chip Plus' system which includes a 6502 microprocessor-based controller illustrated in Fig 11.5.

Table 11.2   Part of instruction set for 6502 microprocessor

Mnemonic	Machine code	Operation
LDA#FF	A9 FF	Load the accumulator with the number FF
STA FE63	8D 63 FE	Store the contents of the accumulator at address FE63
LDY#0C	A0 0C	Put delay length 0C in Y register
JSR delay	20 80 27	Execute delay

Fig 11.5   The '3-Chip Plus' microprocessor board.

11.5 INPUT AND OUTPUT PERIPHERALS

A **peripheral** is the name given to input and output devices used to interface computers to the external environment. Examples of input and output peripherals are given in Table 11.3.

Table 11.3   Input and output peripherals

Input	Output
Keyboard	Visual display unit (VDU) or monitor
Mouse	Printer
Joystick	Plotter
Analogue sensors (ADC needed)	Output transducers such as lamps,
Scanner	motors, etc. (DAC needed to control
Digital sensors	brightness, speed, etc.)
CD ROM	

A **modem** is an example of a peripheral which can be used as both an input and output device. It allows data to be transmitted from or received by a computer via the telephone network.

An item such as a keyboard has well over a hundred switches and it is obviously not possible to connect them all to the computer. A process known as multiplexing is carried out within the keyboard circuitry which 'scans' the keys on a row and column basis and the results are encoded into bytes of information in the ASCII format. The code is transmitted one bit at a time down a single cable to the computer as sets of pulses and this is known as a serial data link. The rate at which the code is sent is measured in bits per second and is called the baud rate. Peripheral devices which transmit or receive only one *bit* of data at a time require a **serial interface** between the peripheral and the **central processing unit** (**CPU**). Other peripherals can transmit or receive one *byte* of data at a time and a **parallel interface** is then needed. A mouse is an example of an input peripheral which needs a serial interface; many printers require a parallel interface.

Computers usually transfer data from one part of the system to another in parallel form, so it is necessary to convert parallel to serial form if data is to be sent from the computer to a serially driven output peripheral. If data is received from a serial-input peripheral, the data must be converted to parallel form. The device which performs these conversions is called a **shift register**.

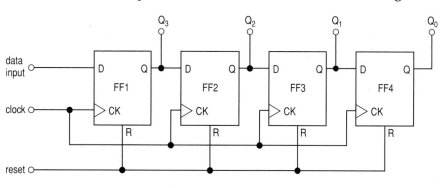

Fig 11.6   A four-bit serial-input shift register.

A shift register consists of several D-type or J–K master–slave flip-flops connected together (see Chapter 7). A four-bit serial-input shift register is shown in Fig 11.6. The resets are connected together so that all the bits can be cleared to 0 at the same time. On the rising edge of each clock pulse the output of each flip-flop assumes the state of its D input.

Q_3	Q_2	Q_1	Q_0	Clock pulse number	
0	0	0	0	0	
1	0	0	0	1	
0	1	0	0	2	
1	0	1	0	3	
1	1	0	1	4	data loaded
0	1	1	0	5	
0	0	1	1	6	
0	0	0	1	7	
0	0	0	0	8	data out

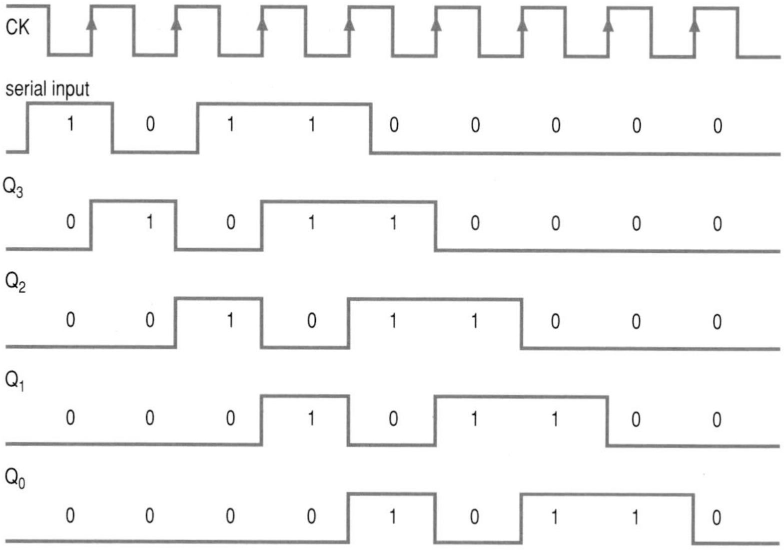

Fig 11.7   Timing diagrams for the four-bit serial-input shift register.

The timing diagrams in Fig 11.7 show what happens if the binary number 1101 (the serial data input) is fed into the first flip-flop by a pulse train. Each clock pulse shifts the data one place to the right in the register. After four clock pulses, each bit of the serial input has been loaded into the register and the device is said to be a **serial-input–parallel-output** type (SIPO) because the outputs Q_3, Q_2, Q_1 and Q_0 are available at the same time. A further four clock pulses enable the data to be shifted out one bit at a time and the device is now said to be a **serial-input–serial-output** type (SISO).

Flip-flops can also be arranged to produce parallel-input-parallel-output (PIPO) and parallel-input-serial output (PISO).

Shift registers are available as integrated circuits. A circuit frequently used for serial input and output is a **Universal Asynchronous Receiver/Transmitter** (UART). It is a register which can be loaded with either serial or parallel data and which will output either serial or parallel data. A modem has a UART IC to convert the parallel data received from the computer to serial form and then transmits the individual bits of a byte along a single line, one after another. Several additional bits of data are also added such as a start bit, to indicate the start of the sequence, a parity bit, for self-checking, and a stop bit, to indicate the end of the sequence. The information is sent to the telephone line by the UART as a sequence of two tones, one tone to represent a '0', the other a '1'. These two tones are produced in the modem from a single tone which is shifted up and down by a set frequency, thus generating two separate tones. The process is called **frequency shift keying** or FSK. A UART in a modem at the receiving end of the link receives the bits of information and reconverts them to bytes which are then sent to the receiving computer.

11.6 THE CENTRAL PROCESSING UNIT

The **central processing unit** (CPU) is manufactured on a single IC called the **microprocessor**. The CPU can be subdivided into three main subsystems: the arithmetic and logic unit, control unit and registers. Fig 11.8 illustrates the main components within the CPU.

The **arithmetic and logic unit** (ALU) carries out calculations and logic operations. Operations available on the ALU include add, subtract, AND, OR and EX-OR.

The **control unit** controls the input and output of data. It is responsible for sequentially fetching instructions from the memory before executing them. A clock pulse generator, usually a crystal oscillator, controls the timing of the whole processor.

The **registers** temporarily store data being processed. When the computer is instructed to 'run', the information in the start address which is stored in the **program counter** is 'fetched'. The value in the program counter is incremented by 1 each time a byte is fetched so that it automatically points to the next instruction.

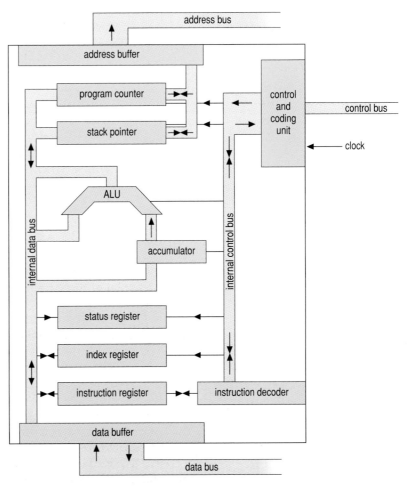

Fig 11.8 Block diagram of typical microprocessor components.

The **instruction register** stores a copy of the current program instruction.

The **stack** is a reserved area of the main memory (RAM) which is used to store information temporarily in a sequential manner so that the latest byte pushed onto the stack is always the first to be pulled from it. The address of the last entry is recorded in the **stack pointer register**.

The **index register** is used as a memory pointer. It could contain the start address of a particular block of data.

The **status** or **flag register** is associated with the ALU. It holds the various flag bits which are set or reset to indicate the condition of registers resulting from the latest instruction or operation.

Typical flags are: carry out, C; negative result, N; result zero, Z; overflow, V. The 'C' flag is set if an arithmetic operation generates a carry, 'N' if the result of an operation is negative, 'Z' if an operation gives a zero result, 'V' if an operation produces an overflow into the sign bit (to indicate polarity).

11.7 MEMORY

In a computer system, memory is either **random-access memory (RAM)** or **read-only memory (ROM)**.

A random-access memory IC has **volatile** memory, which means that data is lost when the power to the IC is disconnected. RAM memory can be written to or read from. There are two main types of RAM IC: **static RAM (SRAM)** and **dynamic RAM (DRAM)**.

A static RAM stores its data in an address until it is changed or lost. The memory stored in a dynamic RAM loses the data over a period of time due to capacitor charge leakage. Additional circuitry is required to ensure that the memory is constantly 'refreshed'.

The 2114 IC in Fig 11.9 is a static RAM containing 4096 flip-flops arranged in 1024 groups of four. This arrangement is so that a nibble from the output of the four flip-fops in a group can be stored in any one of 1024 locations or **addresses** in the memory.

Addresses range from 0 to 1023 (00 0000 0000 to 11 1111 1111 in binary) so the IC has ten address pins, A_0 to A_9. An address is selected by connecting these pins high or low; for example, to select address 00 0000 0001, A_0 is connected to +5 V (logic 1) and all the other address pins are connected to 0 V (logic 0). Data, in the form of a four-bit binary word, can be **written** into an address using the write enable pin ($\overline{WE}$). The IC has four data inputs, D_0 to D_3, one for each bit. Data previously stored in a particular address can then be retrieved or **read** from it by connecting $\overline{WE}$ high. ($\overline{WE}$ is connected low to write and high to read.)

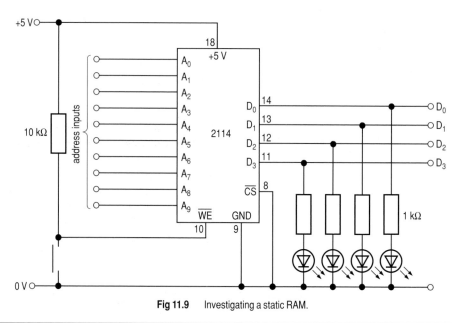

Fig 11.9   Investigating a static RAM.

The static RAM

Construct the circuit in Fig 11.9 on a breadboard using low-current LEDs to display the data. Use 'flying' leads for the address and data inputs.

Write data into various address locations and then read the data from them. The following instructions explain how to do this.

Instructions for writing the word 1011 into address 0000 0000:
1. Connect the ten address input pins to 0 V.
2. Connect the data pins: D_0, D_1 and D_3 to +5 V, and D_2 to 0 V.
3. Connect $\overline{WE}$ momentarily low by pressing and releasing the switch S. This will write the data into the address.

Instructions for reading the word from address 0000 0000:
4. Disconnect all the data input leads. Ensure all address pins are still at 0 V. The LEDs should display the binary word 1011.

The ten wires connected to the address pins of the 2114 SRAM IC are equivalent to the address bus in a computer and the four wires connected to the data pins are equivalent to the data bus. In a computer, there may be several RAM ICs connected to the same address and data buses, so a RAM IC will have a **chip select input** $\overline{CS}$ which is connected low if the IC is the one selected.

A **read-only memory** IC has **non-volatile** (permanent) memory. ROM, as the name suggests, cannot be written to. The ROM in a computer system is used to hold fixed programs and data such as the operating system which is the program by which the computer itself works. When the machine is first switched on the CPU automatically loads the start-up procedures and enables the input and output peripherals; it is called 'booting up' the system.

A **programmable read-only memory** (PROM) IC has a fixed memory which has been programmed by the user.

The program stored on an **erasable programmable read-only memory** (EPROM) can be erased, usually by shining ultraviolet radiation on it. The EPROM can then be reprogrammed.

Electrically erasable PROM (EEPROM) can be electrically modified without the need for a UV light source. This allows a program to be changed while the microchip is in place.

Fig 11.10 represents the complete set of memory locations which can be accessed by a 2^{16} address bus. This graphical representation of the allocation of memory within a computer system is called a memory (or address) map. Memory, particularly RAM memory, is expensive and personal computers (PCs) are often supplied with a nominal number of memory chips fitted, leaving the remaining address space as 'expansion' slots for the users to fit their own quantity of memory when required.

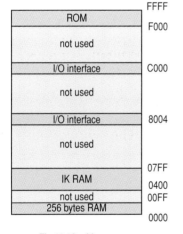

Fig 11.10   Memory map.

11.8 FUTURE DEVELOPMENTS*

One ongoing trend in computer development is microminiaturisation, the effort to compress more circuit elements into smaller and smaller chip space. Researchers are also trying to speed up operations through the use of superconductivity, the phenomenon of decreased electrical resistance observed when objects are exposed to very low temperatures. Another ongoing development is the increase in computer networking, which now also uses satellites to link computers world-wide.

Fuzzy logic is quickly establishing itself as the top growth technology of the 1990s. Fuzzy is a form of logic in which variables can have degrees of

* The text relating to 'fuzzy logic' is taken from *'Which?'* magazine, January 1996, and *Practical Electronics*, October 1991.

truthfulness or falsehood represented by a range of values between 1 (true) and 0 (false). With fuzzy logic, the outcome of an operation can be expressed as a probability rather than as a certainty. Fuzzy logic resembles human decision-making with the ability to generate precise solutions from uncertain information. It is estimated that by the year 2000 more than 90% of microprocessor control equipment will employ fuzzy logic. Some of the most common fuzzy logic applications presently available on the market include washing machines, air conditioning systems, vacuum cleaners and camcorders. In Japan, fuzzy logic controls an underground train service. Washing machines which use fuzzy logic allow the machine to vary the program to suit the washload. It monitors its own performance and fine tunes it if necessary. Work is in progress at present to develop computers that can solve complex problems in what might eventually be called creative ways, the ideal goal being true artificial intelligence. One path actively being explored is a parallel-processing computer, which uses many chips to perform several different tasks at the same time. Parallel processing may eventually be able to duplicate to some degree the complex feedback, approximating and assessing functions of human thought.

SUMMARY

Inputs and outputs of a computer system are called peripherals.

The central processing unit controls the operation of the whole computer system.

The arithmetic and logic unit performs calculations and logic operations.

The CPU is connected to other parts of the system by a bus network.

Data can be stored or shifted using a shift register.

Random-access memory can be written to or read from. RAM is 'forgotten' when power is disconnected.

Read-only memory cannot be changed or erased.

Appendix A

TEST EQUIPMENT AND BREADBOARD CONSTRUCTION

Analogue and digital multimeters are designed to measure voltage, current and resistance. Modern digital multimeters can also measure capacitance, frequency and temperature and can also have a transistor and diode test facility. Digital and analogue meters are compared in Table A.1.

Table A.1   A comparison of digital and analogue meters

Digital meter	Analogue meter
Needs its own power supply	Needs no power supply
Resistance measurement uses the same scale as voltage and current measurements	Resistance scales are not linear and require a separate battery
Cheap, robust	Expensive, delicate moving-coil mechanism
Very high resistance	Meter resistance depends on the range used – lower than for a digital meter

The main advantage of the digital meter is its high input resistance, which makes it ideal as a voltmeter, so that negligible current is drawn from the component across which the voltage is being measured. The main advantage of the analogue meter over a digital one is that it can display a changing voltage such as the charging of a capacitor.

Precautions to be taken when using a digital meter

When measuring current, select the largest full-scale deflection setting since the fuse inside the meter will melt if you select a scale which is smaller than the current being measured. When you have an indication of the actual size of the current being measured you can then select an appropriate scale to give you a more precise reading. Some meters have an 'auto-range' facility which automatically selects the best scale to use.

Breadboard construction

A prototype board or breadboard enables you to develop and test a circuit, since the components are not permanently fixed to the board, allowing changes to be made. Fig A.1 shows how the connections are made on a small section of breadboard. The holes in the breadboard are separated by 0.1 inch (2.54 mm) to allow integrated circuits to be used. Each integrated circuit in use must be inserted into the breadboard so that it straddles the centre of the board where there are no connections between the upper and the lower set of five holes You must make sure that both ends of any component are never connected in the same vertical line of five holes because, if it were, the component would be short-circuited by the connection between the five holes, shown by the red lines. The top rail of the breadboard is connected to the positive terminal of the battery and the bottom rail to 0 V.

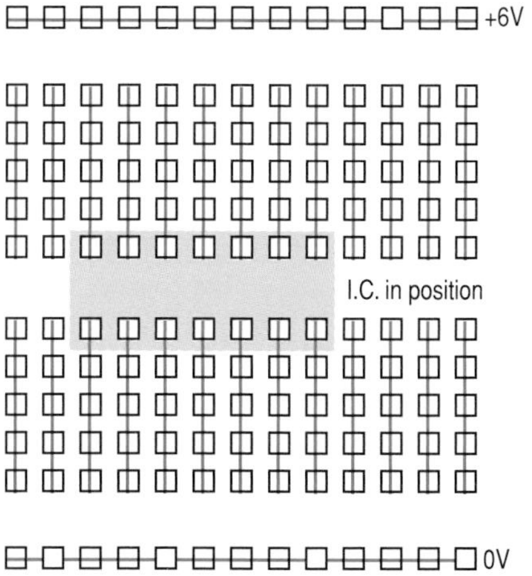

Fig A.1 How connections are made on a breadboard.

Appendix B

DATA FOR COMMON CMOS AND TTL INTEGRATED CIRCUITS

Table B.1 gives information about the supply, input and output voltages of some of the common logic ICs used in electronic circuits. Further electrical data can be obtained from component data sheets.

Table B.1   Supply, input and output voltages of four common logic ICs

| Type | Logic family | Supply voltage/V | For a supply voltage of 5 V | | | |
| | | | Input voltage/V | | Output voltage/V | |
			Logic 0	Logic 1	Logic 0	Logic 1
4000B	CMOS	3.0–18.0	0–1.5	3.5–5.0	0	5.0
74HC	CMOS	2.0–6.0	0–0.9	3.6–5.0	0–0.4	4.2–5.0
74HCT	CMOS	5.0	0–0.8	2.0–5.0	0–0.4	3.5–5.0
74LS	TTL	5.0	0–0.8	2.0–5.0	0–0.5	2.7–5.0

There are some points to note:

- The ranges of input and output voltages for CMOS 4000B series and 74HC series depend on the supply voltage used. The ranges quoted in Table B.1 are for a supply voltage of 5.0 V. For the 4000B series a supply voltage V_{DD} will give a logic 0 input range from 0 V to $0.3V_{DD}$ and a logic 1 input range from $0.7V_{DD}$ to V_{DD}.
- 74HCT series are CMOS ICs with TTL compatible inputs.

Fig B.1 illustrates the low and high input and output levels for the 74HC series if $V_{DD} = 5$ V and $V_{SS} = 0$ V. For reliable operation you must avoid operating the IC at voltages within the **indeterminate zone**.

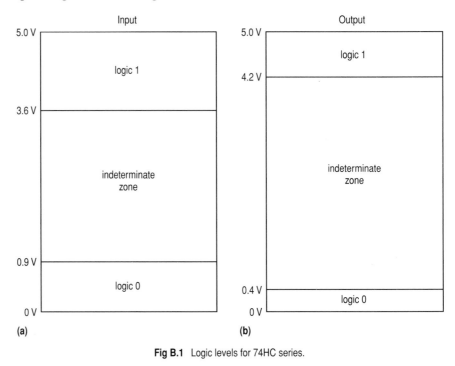

Fig B.1   Logic levels for 74HC series.

Appendix C

EXAMINATION QUESTIONS

1. (a) Explain the difference between a **full-adder** and a **half-adder**.
    (b) Show how the following two Boolean expressions describe the behaviour of the half-adder

    $$S = (A + B).\overline{A.B} \qquad C = A.B$$

    where S = sum, C = carry and A and B are the inputs.
    (c) Construct a truth table for the full-adder
    (d) Derive a Boolean expression for the carry from the full-adder.
    (Oxford and Cambridge Schools Examination Board, June 1994)

2. The circuit in Fig C.1 was designed for use in a factory which needs to restrict access of its workers to various areas. Each worker has a card to insert into a reader to operate one or more switches, sending the worker's code to the circuit.

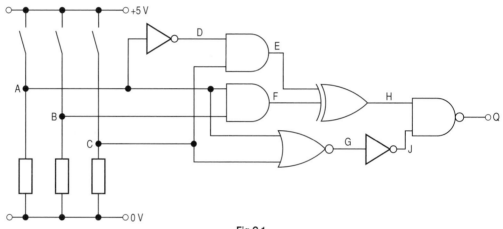

Fig C.1

    (a) Construct a truth table for the circuit.
    (b) Show that the output can be expressed as $(\overline{A}.C) + (A.B)$ and hence show that

    $$\left[(\overline{A}.C) \oplus (A.B)\right].(A + C) = (\overline{A}.C) + (A.B)$$

    (c) Draw the circuit diagram for a system of NAND gates with the same function as the circuit above, but using no more than five dual input gates.
    (d) Design a circuit which will allow access to a different part of the factory just to card holders whose cards close switch C only, or which close all three switches. Show the stages in your design.
    (Oxford and Cambridge Schools Examination Board, February 1995)

3. This question is about resonance in an electrical circuit.

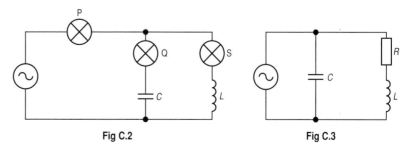

Fig C.2   **Fig C.3**

A variable-frequency oscillator is connected to a pure capacitor C and a pure inductance L in parallel as shown in Fig C.2. Three small indicator lamps, P, Q and S, monitor the currents in the circuit.

(a) Explain briefly, by considering the reactances of the components, the following observations:

    (i)   at low frequencies P and S glow but Q does not,

    (ii) at high frequencies P and Q glow but S does not,

    (iii) at one particular frequency Q and S glow but P does not.

(b) In a practical circuit the inductor has resistance as well as inductance. Describe the effect on the resonant behaviour of including resistance R in the circuit of Fig C.3.

(Oxford and Cambridge Schools Examination Board, June 1995)

4.   (a) Draw labelled sketch graphs to show how the frequency response of an operational amplifier varies with the amount of negative feedback.

(b) The circuit of Fig C.4 shows an amplifier with negative feedback, the magnitude of which varies with the illumination of the LDR.

If the maximum and minimum values of resistance R_L of the LDR are $500\,\text{k}\Omega$ and $4.0\,\text{k}\Omega$, calculate the range of values over which V_{OUT} could vary when V_{IN} is constant at $+0.1\,\text{V}$. State what happens as the illumination goes from high to low and suggest an application for the circuit.

(c) Describe how you would use a unity-gain voltage follower, together with a high-value resistor R, to study the current/potential difference characteristic of a silicon diode for **reverse** voltages of up to $12\,\text{V}$. Your answer should include a circuit diagram.

Give a typical value for R and the range of any meters employed. You may assume that the maximum reverse current in the diode is a few nanoamperes.

(University of London Examinations and Assessment Council, June 1994)

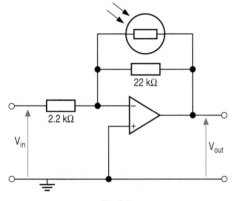

22 kΩ

2.2 kΩ

V_{in}

V_{out}

Fig C.4

5.   (a) Under what circumstances is a transistor said to be saturated?

(b) Under what circumstances is a transistor said to be switched off?

(c) The transistor in Fig C.5 has a d.c. current gain (h_{FE}) of 200.

    (i)   Show that when the transistor is saturated the collector current is $1\,\text{mA}$.

    (ii) Calculate the emitter voltage when the transistor is just saturated.

    (iii) Calculate the minimum input voltage V_{IN} required to saturate the transistor.

    (iv) Draw a sketch graph of the output voltage V_{OUT} as a function of the input voltage V_{IN} as the potentiometer wiper is moved from one extreme to the other.

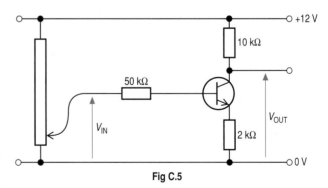

+12 V

10 kΩ

50 kΩ

V_{IN}

V_{OUT}

2 kΩ

0 V

Fig C.5

(d) A second transistor is added to the circuit of Fig C.5 so that it shares the same emitter resistor. The modification is shown in Fig C.6 where both transistors have d.c. current gains of 200.

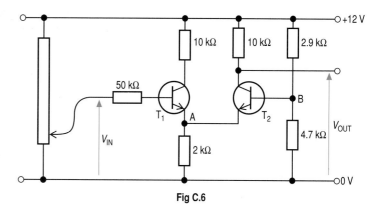

Fig C.6

(i) Show that the voltage at point B is 1.7 V.
(ii) Calculate the voltage at point A when the input voltage V_{IN} is set to zero. Explain your working.
(iii) Calculate the output voltage V_{OUT} when the input voltage V_{IN} is set to zero. Explain your working.
(iv) Calculate the voltages at A and V_{OUT} when the input V_{IN} is set to 12 V. Explain your working.
(v) Estimate the minimum input voltage V_{IN} required to switch off transistor T_2. Explain your working.
(vi) Draw a sketch graph of the output voltage V_{OUT} as a function of the input voltage V_{IN} as the potentiometer wiper is moved from one extreme to the other.

(University of Cambridge Local Examinations Syndicate, June 1995)

6. Fig C.7 represents the apparatus used to measure the rate of flow of liquid into a graduated flask. The apparatus consists of two reflective opto-switches A and B connected to an exclusive-OR gate. The output from the gate is used to trigger a time clock.
    (a) (i) Name the **two** parts in an opto-switch.
    (ii) In a reflective opto-switch the two parts are placed alongside each other. State how this arrangement allows the level of the liquid to be detected.
    (iii) Give **one** advantage of using an opto-switch rather than electrodes immersed in the liquid.
    (b) Complete the truth table for an EX-OR gate.
    (c) Bearing in mind your answers to parts (a) and (b) explain how each part of the system enables the time taken for the liquid to rise from level 1 to level 2 to be measured.

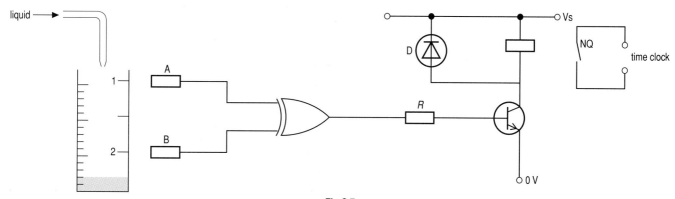

Fig C.7

(d) State the function in the circuit of resistor R.
(e) State the function in the circuit of the diode D. Explain how the diode achieves its function.

(Northern Examinations and Assessment Board, June 1995)

Appendix D

NUMERICAL ANSWERS TO QUESTIONS

In-text questions

Chapter 1

1.1	0.11 mA
1.2	1.45 V
1.3	50 Hz
1.4	325 V
1.5	24 V
1.6	13.0 A

Chapter 2

2.1	**(a)** Orange orange green silver **(b)** Brown green black red brown
2.2	**(a)** 100RJ **(b)** 5K6K
2.3	No, a power rating greater than 0.54 W is required ($>1.5 \times 0.36$ W)
2.4	6.6 kΩ (6.8 kΩ)
2.5	68 Ω
2.6	29 kΩ
2.7	0.517 µF, 0.423 µF
2.8	0.594 F, 0.264 F
2.9	0.19 µF
2.10	**(a)** 0.76 µF **(b)** 15.7 µF
2.11	4.7 s
2.12	5.7 V
2.13	**(a)** 10 s **(b)** 3.16 V **(c)** 2.26 V
2.14	0.72
2.15	396 s
2.16	0.034 J
2.17	**(a)** 677 Ω **(b)** 67.7 Ω
2.18	**(a)** 15.7 Ω **(b)** 157 Ω

Chapter 3

3.1	0.51 A, 50
3.2	**(a)** 1.05 mA **(b)** 107 mA **(c)** 103
3.3	22 mA
3.4	2 kΩ (2.2 kΩ preferred)
3.5	1 kΩ

Chapter 4

4.1	**(a)** 1 kΩ **(b)** 7 kΩ
4.2	**(a)** 4.78 V **(b)** 0.10 V
4.3	0.5 kΩ, 5 °C
4.4	1.25 V, 4.24 V

4.5

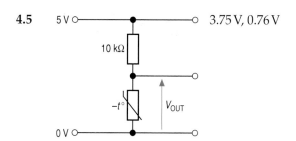

5 V ○————————○ 3.75 V, 0.76 V

10 kΩ

$-t°$ V_{OUT}

0 V ○————————○

4.6 −0.105 V

4.7 When the temperature of the thermistor rises above a certain value, the transistor switches on, energising the relay. The switch contacts close and the motor switches on.

Chapter 5

5.1 (a) 15 (b) 16 (c) 19 (d) 31 (e) 37

5.2 (a) 0101 (b) 0001 0101 (c) 0100 0100 (d) 1000 1000 (e) 1111 1110

5.3 $\overline{A}.B.C \oplus A.\overline{B}.C$

5.4

A	B	$\overline{B}$	A.B	$A.\overline{B}$	$A.B + A.\overline{B}$
0	0	1	0	0	0
0	1	0	0	0	0
1	0	1	0	1	1
1	1	0	1	0	1

5.5 $\overline{\overline{A.\overline{B}}.B} + \overline{\overline{A}.B.B}$

A	B	$\overline{A.\overline{B}}$	$\overline{\overline{A.\overline{B}}.B}$	Q
0	0	1	1	0
0	1	1	0	1
1	0	1	1	0
1	1	0	1	0

$$\overline{\overline{A.\overline{B}}.B} + \overline{\overline{A}.B.B} = \overline{\overline{\overline{A.\overline{B}}.B} + \overline{\overline{A}.B.B}}$$

$$= \overline{\overline{A.\overline{B}}.B} \ . \ \overline{\overline{A}.B.B}$$

$$= B.\overline{A.\overline{B}}$$

$$= B.\left(\overline{A} + B\right)$$

$$= B.\overline{A}$$

A	B	$\overline{A}$	Q
0	0	1	0
0	1	1	1
1	0	0	0
1	1	0	0

5.6 $\overline{(A + B).\left(\overline{B}.A\right)} = \overline{A + B} + \overline{\overline{B}.A}$

$$= \left(\overline{A}.\overline{B}\right) + \left(\overline{\overline{B}} + \overline{A}\right)$$

$$= \overline{A}.\overline{B} + \left(B + \overline{A}\right)$$

$$= \overline{A}.\left(\overline{B} + 1\right) + B$$

$$= \overline{A} + B$$

5.7

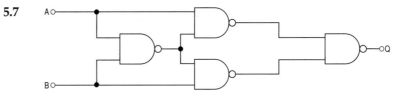

5.8

Inputs from counters				Outputs							Display
A_3	A_2	A_1	A_0	a	b	c	d	e	f	g	
0	0	1	1	1	1	1	1	0	0	1	3
0	1	0	0	0	1	1	0	0	1	1	4
0	1	0	1	1	0	1	1	0	1	1	5
0	1	1	0	1	0	1	1	1	1	1	6
0	1	1	1	1	1	1	0	0	1	0	7
1	0	0	0	1	1	1	1	1	1	1	8
1	0	0	1	1	1	1	1	0	1	1	9

Chapter 6

6.1 11.4 s
6.2 $R = 13.6\,k\Omega$ (15 kΩ preferred)
6.3 $R_1 = R_2 = 9.5\,k\Omega$ (10 kΩ preferred)
6.4 Using $R_1 = R_2 = 9.5\,k\Omega$, $C = 1\,\mu F$

Chapter 7

7.1

$\overline{S}$	$\overline{R}$	Q
1	0	0
1	1	0
0	1	1
1	1	1
0	1	1

7.2 256

Chapter 8

8.1 3 dB
8.2 **(a)** 10 000 **(b)** 44 670 **(c)** 199 500 **(d)** 1000 **(e)** 100
8.3 Power gain (in dB) = 10 log 0.5 = −3 dB
8.4 18 mV
8.5 **(a)** 3.06 V **(b)** 3.06 mA **(c)** 0.02 mA **(d)** 5.94 mW

Chapter 9

9.1

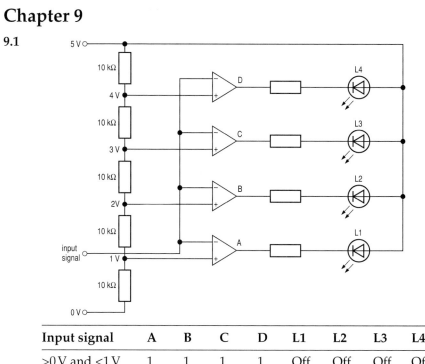

Input signal	A	B	C	D	L1	L2	L3	L4
>0 V and <1 V	1	1	1	1	Off	Off	Off	Off
>1 V and <2 V	0	1	1	1	On	Off	Off	Off
>2 V and <3 V	0	0	1	1	On	On	Off	Off
>3 V and <4 V	0	0	0	1	On	On	On	Off
>4 V and <5 V	0	0	0	0	On	On	On	On

9.2   **(a)** 100   **(b)** 10
9.3 $40\,k\Omega$,   **(a)** 15 mV   **(b)** 2.5 V   **(c)** 13.5 V (saturation)
9.4 $100\,k\Omega$,   **(a)** −10 mV   **(b)** −5 mV   **(c)** −13.5 V (saturation)
9.5   754.5 Hz

Chapter 10

10.1   −2.475 V

10.2

Binary input code				Analogue output/V
0	0	0	0	0.0000
0	0	0	1	−0.0625
0	0	1	0	−0.1250
0	0	1	1	−0.1875
0	1	0	0	−0.2500
0	1	0	1	−0.3125
0	1	1	0	−0.3750
0	1	1	1	−0.4375
1	0	0	0	−0.5000
1	0	0	1	−0.5625
1	0	1	0	−0.6250
1	0	1	1	−0.6875
1	1	0	0	−0.7500
1	1	0	1	−0.8125
1	1	1	0	−0.8750
1	1	1	1	−0.9375

10.3   **(a)** −0.10 V   **(b)** −1.55 V

Chapter 11

11.1   **(a)** 255   **(b)** 75   **(c)** 1482   **(d)** 3642
11.2   **(a)** 11   **(b)** 5A   **(c)** EF   **(d)** D0A
11.3   **(a)** 2F   **(b)** 36   **(c)** AB   **(d)** FF
11.4   **(a)** 1111 1110   **(b)** 0100 1011   **(c)** 0101 1100 1010   **(d)** 1110 0011 1010

Numerical answers to examination questions

4   **(b)** −0.15 to −0.96 V
5   **(c)** (ii)   2.0 V
         (iii) 2.95 V
     (d) (ii)   1.0 V
         (iii) 7.0 V
         (iv) 2.0 V, 12.0 V
         (v)   > 1.83 V

Appendix E

FURTHER READING AND RESOURCES

Suppliers of tools, components, test equipment

Commotion
  Unit 11, Tannery Road, Tonbridge, Kent TN9 1RF

Farnell Electronic Components Ltd
  Canal Road, Leeds LS12 2TU

JPR Electronics Ltd
  Unit M, Kingsway Industrial Estate, Kingsway, Luton, Bedfordshire LU1 1LP

Maplin Electronic Supplies Ltd
  PO Box 3, Rayleigh, Essex SS6 8LR

Rapid Electronics Ltd
  Heckworth Close, Severalls Industrial Estate, Colchester, Essex CO4 4TB

RS Components
  PO Box 99, Corby, Northamptonshire NN17 9RS

Systems kits

Omega Electronics
  12 Oxhill Road, Middle Tysoe, Warwickshire CV35 0SX

Unilab Ltd
  The Science Park, Hutton Street, Blackburn BB1 3BT

Computer software

'Crocodile Clips' enables you to design schematic animated circuits. Unlike laboratory work, there are no faulty components and loose connections to worry about. This means that you can learn basic concepts of electronics and electricity more quickly and clearly.

Crocodile Clips
  11 Randolph Place, Edinburgh EH3 7TA

'Quickroute 3.5' is a PCB and schematic design system for Windows.

Quickroute Systems Ltd
  14 Ley Lane, Marple Bridge, Stockport SK6 5DD

Periodicals

Physics Review
Philip Allan Publishers
  Market Place, Deddington, Oxfordshire OX15 0SE

Electronics Education
IEE
  PO Box 96, Stevenage, Herts SG1 2SD

Everyday Practical Electronics
Wimbourne Publishing Ltd
  Allen House, East Borough, Wimbourne, Dorset BH21 1PF

Index